SECRETS OF THE COSMETIC INDUSTRY REVEALED

NATURAL Spa PRODUCTS

*How to make your own professional and home spa products
using natural ingredients*

KOLBJØRN BORSETH

Published by Aromantic Ltd

17 Tytler Street, Forres, Moray, IV36 1EL, Scotland

Tel: +44 (0)1309 696900 Fax: +44 (0)1309 696911

E-mail: info@aromantic.co.uk

Websites: www.aromantic.co.uk, www.aromantic.com

© Copyright 2010, Aromantic

ISBN 978-0-9554323-4-7

ABOUT THE AUTHOR

Originally from Norway, Kolbjørn Borseth is the founder of Aromantic Natural Skin Care and has been working with and developing natural skin, hair and body care products since he started his factory in Sweden in 1985. His passion is to reveal the secrets that the cosmetic industry would rather hide from us. He now teaches others how to make their own products using natural raw materials tailor-made for their friends, family or clients. He does this by providing in-depth information about raw materials on his website, in recipe brochures, press articles, educational guides, books and running educational courses. He is also the author of *The Aromantic Guide to the use of Herbs in Skin, Hair and Health Care products*, *The Aromantic Guide to making your own Natural Skin, Hair and Body Care products* and *The Aromantic Guide to Unlocking the Powerful Health and Rejuvenation Benefits of Vegetable Oils*.

ACKNOWLEDGEMENTS

As always, I would like to thank Finn Andersen of Crearome, Sweden, who started me out on this journey, when I attended one of his early courses in Stockholm in the mid-1980s.

My gratitude and fond affection to the late Lilly Johansson, with whom I worked, and learnt so much from, for 10 years in Scandinavia, where she was a health icon.

My wife Helena, and my family, who are supportive in their understanding that for me teaching and sharing this knowledge is not a hobby, or even work…but a mission.

All of my loyal and hard-working colleagues at Aromantic who have always supported me, with special thanks to my 'right-hand', Monika Dachs.

Susan Kemp, thank you for your excellent research, organising, editing and proofreading skills, in this, our first book for the public. May there be many more…

Elspeth Barker, for kindly testing products in the book and providing valuable feedback which made this book a better one.

Mike Harmon and Hassina Dadamiya, thank you both for your vital support you give to me in many aspects of my work.

And last but not least, my customers. Many of you are my friends; all of you have inspired me to develop this knowledge further. If not for your continual support that you offer through the buying of our raw materials, I couldn't afford to research and develop these books.

CONTENTS

INTRODUCTION

INTRODUCTION

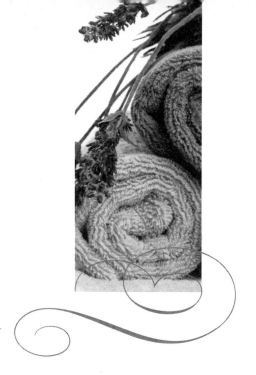

HISTORY OF THE SPA & BATHING CULTURE

TIPS FOR A HOME SPA

SELLING YOUR SPA PRODUCTS

USEFUL EQUIPMENT FOR MAKING YOUR SPA PRODUCTS

BALANCING YOUR BODY CHEMISTRY

KNEIPP HYDROTHERAPY TREATMENT

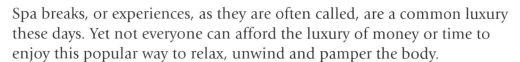

Spa breaks, or experiences, as they are often called, are a common luxury these days. Yet not everyone can afford the luxury of money or time to enjoy this popular way to relax, unwind and pamper the body.

The popularity of the spa experience does however present opportunities for you to sell professional spa products. This book contains many recipes that can be used by professionals such as beauticians and body therapists to make commercial spa products to sell to their clients or to the public for home use.

But of course you don't have to be a professional to enjoy making these high quality products – anyone can make them! You may simply want to recreate the spa experience at home and make these products for you and your family and friends to enjoy. If you're new to making your own products, start with the more simple recipes in this book, some of them are pure kitchen cosmetics and really easy to make; try the more difficult ones as you gain confidence.

Whatever you choose to make, you'll find the recipes easy to follow with step-by-methods and tips for successful spa products!

HISTORY OF SPA & BATHING CULTURE

Many civilisations and cultures originated around large rivers and in locations where these rivers met the sea. People relied on rivers like the Indus, Yangtze, Nile, Euphrates and Tigris for their survival. These rivers nourished the earth and it was believed that they could also make women fertile and give older people vitality. They were often looked upon as holy places that could enhance health and well being.

On my travels I have been to some of the most important bathing places in the world where ritual cleansing is carried out. The ritual temple baths at Mohenjo-Daro, the capital of the Indus culture, dates back to 2500 BCE. The whole town was built around a big pool where people could bathe ritually. Even the private houses in those days had baths.

Today the Ganges River in India is the biggest ritual bathing place in the world. Waking up to the noise of India one morning in Varanasi and seeing the Hindu pilgrims bathing in the Ganges and offering lotus flowers is a special sight that I will never forget.

Baptism is a very old ritual where the whole person is submerged in water. John the Baptist is said to have baptised newly born Christians in the Jordan river.

Egyptian priests had two ritual baths in the morning and two in the evening and there have been many archaeological discoveries pointing to a strong Egyptian bathing culture. Soap was invented in Babylon around 1000 BCE so that the water was even better utilised for cleansing and cleaning purposes.

In Greece on the Island of Crete a bathroom has been found which contains a bathtub built for King Minos of Knossos around 2000 BCE. Hippocrates looked upon the bath as an important part of the cure to balance the fluids of the body. In the *Iliad*, Homer often mentions the Greek's passion for bathing. It is believed that the people of Laconica, the ancient region of Greece that had Sparta as its capital city, conceived the idea of bathing culture.

The Greek bath culture varied throughout its history and in different stages included fasting, usually followed by a bath, then offerings, and prayers. Prior to exercising or to athletic contests, male Greek contestants would lubricate their bodies with olive oil. This reduced the number of minor skin injuries and helped to keep the pores free from dirt. After physical training or an athletic contest, the athletes would scrape the film of oil, sweat and dirt off their bodies using a curved, metal instrument called a *strigil*, which appear often in vase paintings. The *strigil* was used in ancient Greece and Rome for general cleansing. First perfumed oil was applied to the skin, and then it would be scraped off, along with the dirt. *Strigils*

were often used in Roman baths and slaves often had to scrape off the dirt from their wealthy owners' bodies.

The Romans learned about baths from the Greeks when they came into contact with them approximately 500 BCE. They adapted the Greek ideas and built bath house complexes available to all due to the cheap price of admission. Rome, with over a million inhabitants, had nearly 900 official bath houses. In the larger complexes, there were different types of rooms and pools and an exercise area and typically a slave undressed you and then you took your first cooling bath in a cold pool called a *fridgidarium*. From there you moved into the warm bath called the *tepidarium*. After that you could then stretch out on benches in the *caldarium*, where baths of hot water sunk into the floor were heated by an underfloor heating system and there was sometimes even a *laconicum*, a very hot and dry room like a sauna.

After either the *caldarium* or *laconicum*, you were taken into the next room, where the temperature was a little cooler so that massage could be carried out. You were then thoroughly rinsed with cold water in the *labrum* and then finally you would go to the *unctuarium* where you would have olive oil and perfumes rubbed onto your skin by one of the slaves owned by the baths. These perfumed oils were homemade

or bought from ointment producers known as *unguentarii* (men) *or unguentariae* (women). This procedure would often take the whole day in the company of friends. The largest bath house complex could accommodate up to 1500 people at a time and were important social meeting places for men. Women mostly had their baths at home. Baths were so much a part of life that almost every town had at least one bath, which served as centres of public swimming and social interaction. Throughout the Roman Empire, bathing complexes appeared where there were natural hot springs, including Britain, Ireland, Germany, Algeria, and the Netherlands. Here, the Romans bathed, exercised and socialised with each other.

With the fall of the Roman Empire and the success of the highly puritanical Christian culture, bathing culture faded away. The bath houses or similar complexes were generally closed down by the Christian church during the dark ages. It is now thought that sexual diseases were transmitted in the bath houses at the time. It was also believed then that 'real Christians' should not wash and be clean; the dirtier they were, the more holy they were believed to be and so they rarely bathed. This is evidenced by many stories of the Crusades against the Muslims. It was thought that Jews or Muslims must have influenced people who cleansed themselves by bathing. People were often burned at the stake for being too clean! Unfortunately, a lot of diseases were spread because of this uncleanliness.

When the Ottoman Turks conquered Alexandria in Egypt 1517 ACE, they enjoyed the Roman baths and modified the idea of having hot baths to having hot steam baths, also known as *hammams*. This was the origination of the Turkish bath.

From the eighteenth century BCE onwards, the development of medicine meant that a more scientific and analytical approach was taken towards researching the properties and composition of water and so therapeutic hydrotherapy entered a new age. Between the nineteenth and twentieth centuries, spas became the preserve of the privileged European social class. It was later that the spa phenomenon became available to other social classes. Inspired by the Russian saunas, or *banyas*, the English started to build public baths for lower and middle classes in the 1820s. The public bath movement, which started in England in the 1920s subsequently influenced baths being built from the public purse for the lower and middle classes elsewhere in Europe and in America. In England, the first indoor public bath built for the people at public expense was the St. George's Bath in Liverpool, opened in 1828. By 1896, there were over 200 public baths in the British Isles, most of which had public laundry facilities as well. Victorian Turkish baths were first introduced to Ireland by David Urquhart, the Scottish diplomat and one-time Member of Parliament for Stafford in England, who was partly responsible for the opening of the first modern Turkish bath in county Cork in 1856. Soon after Turkish baths sprang up rapidly throughout the

north and midlands of England due to a well-organised political Turkish bath movement there. It was only a few years later that Turkish baths appeared in London. It is believed that about 300 Turkish baths were built during the Victorian era. The dryness of the air in the Victorian Turkish bath actually made them more similar to a reinvented Roman bath than a Turkish bath used in Turkey.

By 1891 smaller numbers of municipal baths could also be found in most European countries, including Belgium, Holland, Italy, Hungary, Norway, and Sweden. Around the same time, Buenos Aires was the only place in South America to have a municipal bath. In the United States of America, the demand for public baths became evident in the 1840s mainly because of the poverty and filthy living conditions of the urban poor. The high levels of poor living conditions were due to a number of factors, such as the 'Panic of 1837' and the subsequent banking collapse and 5-year economic depression, the massive numbers of Irish immigrants who were fleeing the famine in Ireland, and urban growth. In the 30-year period of 1830-1850 the major US cities of New York, Philadelphia and Boston more than doubled in the sizes of their populations. The public baths were therefore built for the benefit of the lower classes, whereas in Britain, Ireland and Europe the baths mainly benefited the middle classes as the lower classes often found these places quite intimidating and expensive. The American middle classes could see the benefits of regular bathing but tended to install bathrooms into their own homes. There the habit of regular bathing turned into a water cure craze of the 1840s and '50s, which strengthened the association between good health and regular bathing but had the additional healthy elements of drinking water, exercise and simple diet.

The word 'spa' is said to come from a municipality in Belgium called Spa, in the province of Liège. Around 1400 CE it became famous for its mineral rich hot springs and mud baths. Drinking the water was an important part of the therapy. The spa town inspired small hotels to provide different types of diets and treatments. This movement helped to make vegetarian diets popular in modern times. In time, these hotels became more like health centres. The hotels drew many famous healers to them, such as the priest Kneipp (1821-1897). Kneipp spas were subsequently built all over Europe.

It is an amazing fact, however, that when Queen Victoria was crowned in 1837, there was not one bathroom in Buckingham Palace! After 1900 ACE bathtubs became popular in flats and houses all over Europe. Now European countries (except the United Kingdom) are abandoning the bathtub in favour of the shower.

Only in remote areas such as northern Russia, Estonia and Finland has the bathing habit continued undisturbed to this day. Sauna-goers, both men and women, sit naked in a small wooden hut with temperatures ranging from 60-100°C. Typically fresh birch branches are then used to whisk and stimulate the blood flow to the skin. Afterwards they cool down by rolling in the snow or taking a dip in a cold lake. The entire process is then repeated. Public saunas are now popular and well used throughout the world and are often found in indoor leisure complexes and hotels. However, customers usually wear bathing costumes, which some consider unsanitary, and don't have much opportunity to roll around in

the snow afterwards! There is said to be about three saunas to every ten people in Finland today!

Different cultures such as Persia, China and Japan still have different bath rituals. It is recorded in *The History of the Kingdom of Wei* that the Japanese engaged in ritual bathing as early as 297 CE. Natural hot springs, called *onsen*, are still highly popular across Japan today and there are 20,000 hot springs found in every region of the country.

In recent years we have seen a renaissance of health spas in urban and country areas all over Europe. You can now choose to pamper yourself with an expensive spa resort break, attend a day spa, buy very expensive spa products or make them yourself.

This book contains many recipes for spa products for health, healing and beauty that you can easily make at home using nature-friendly ingredients.

Tips for a Home Spa

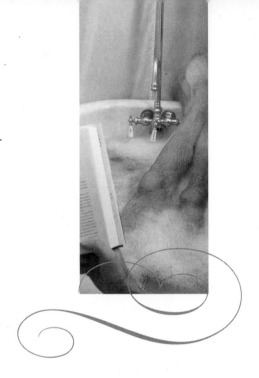

If you plan to have a spa experience at home, I have a few tips that will make the time you have set aside for relaxing and pampering yourself much more enjoyable.

Plan Your Spa Experience in Advance

This is particularly important if you have a busy schedule or if you share a house with others. You can decide to take a morning, afternoon or evening or even the whole day, depending on your commitments. Whatever you decide, stick to it. Decide to take the time just for you. If you have children, arrange for child care or alternative activities for your children. You wouldn't pay for an expensive spa break and leave halfway through the break without a very good reason, so don't do it at home either! Buy the ingredients or make the products you need in advance and unclutter your treatment and quiet spaces i.e. your bathroom and either the living room, patio or garden.

Solo or Company?

Decide whether you want to have the spa break on your own, or whether you want to invite a friend or your partner. It all depends on what you're in the mood for. If you want to spend some intimate time with your partner, this might be an ideal way to do it. Or if you have a good friend a spa experience might be a different way of meeting up. Either option provides somebody to give you a massage during your mini spa break. Just be prepared to return the favour! If you prefer to be on your own but would still like to have a massage, you could always make a home appointment with a massage therapist during your home spa experience.

Choose a Spa Theme

Choosing a theme will help you to decide which products to make, which essential oils or ingredients to use and which music to play. Some examples of themes are detoxing, relaxing, rejuvenating, uplifting, stimulating, romantic, etc. You could also decide a theme based on which parts of your body you want to focus on, for example face and upper body, legs, hands and feet, or a whole body experience. It's up to you to decide! Once you have, choose the recipes from this book and prepare a routine for your spa experience.

Rest Before & After

Have a good rest the night before and after your spa experience. This will ensure that you make the most of the time you've set aside just for you.

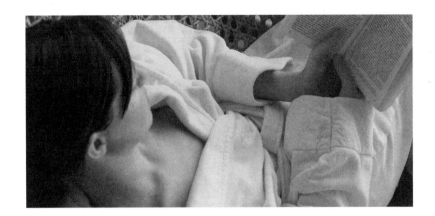

Read an inspiring book, meditate or simply sit quietly…

CREATE A SANCTUARY OF PEACE & RELAXATION

Light some candles, play atmospheric music appropriate for your spa theme, take the phone off the hook, switch the radio, computer and television off and no, don't even check your text messages! Be yourself and enjoy taking this uninterrupted time for yourself.

STAY WARM & DRINK PLENTY OF WATER

Wrap yourself up warmly after or inbetween your spa treatments and relax quietly in your designated 'quiet area'. In cold weather, this could be your living room or bedroom and in good weather, it could be your patio or garden. Read an inspiring book, meditate or simply sit quietly. Drink plenty of water and herbal teas appropriate for your spa theme during your spa experience and for a day or two after.

ENJOY YOUR SPA PRODUCTS EVERY DAY

You don't have to wait until you can take time off to enjoy a home spa experience. You can incorporate the use of the products you make into your everyday wellbeing and beauty routine. Want a cleansing bath? Just reach for your bath salts and put some in the bath water. Need to relax? Have a facial steam with lavender and chamomile flowers. Make a daily habit of cleansing, toning and moisturising your skin. Tired or stressed? It only takes a few minutes to prepare and enjoy the benefits of a foot bath. Set aside an extra hour of preparation time before a night out and have an aromatic bath and facial. You get the idea…

These are just some ideas to get you started. Use your creative imagination and enjoy the adventure!

SELLING YOUR SPA PRODUCTS

....

As they become aware of health and environmental issues, an increasing number of consumers are interested in buying natural, non-allergenic, nature-friendly and preferably organic personal care products. Sales of these products have rocketed since the late 1990s, and continue to surge. There is an increasing trend for even over-the-counter, big brand cosmetics and beauty products to be organic and natural. Whilst the majority of the market is dominated by multinational cosmetic corporations, more and more people enjoy supporting cottage industries and small, local businesses and buying products that are ethical, eco-friendly and economical.

In this book you'll find recipes for spa products that are suitable for selling professionally such as bath salts, fizzy bath bombs, creams, anti-aging eye oils, serums, etc. Although some products are already customised for different purposes, you can customise them further according to your clients' or customers' requirements.

In this book you'll also find recipes for products to be used immediately, such as fruit and vegetable masks, or those that will keep for up to six months, such as flaxseed gel. I share secrets with you on how to extend the shelf life of your products as well as how to optimise the ingredients. At the back of the book I have a short list of resources, including stockists of the ingredients or raw materials. Having run courses

teaching people to make their own cosmetics and beauty products for over 10 years, I know you'll just love making these products. Selling the professional, natural spa products that you make can be very rewarding, fun, creative and fulfilling as many of my course participants and customers can attest to over the years I have been working in this business. I am very pleased to offer you this opportunity to start your own successful business, making and selling natural spa products.

LEGAL ISSUES

Before selling your products to the public over the counter, there are a few different areas that need addressing before you are able to sell your products legally. However, if you're a qualified therapist prescribing products for your clients, or you only want to sell to your family and friends, then it is much easier and simple.

SELLING YOUR SPA PRODUCTS TO YOUR THERAPY CLIENTS

As I said before, this is the simplest option. If you're an aromatherapist, beautician or any other therapist, you can tailor-make natural cosmetics specific to their clients' needs and sell to them directly. Most likely your therapy insurance will cover you for this but check with your insurer first.

HOMECRAFTING – MAKING PRODUCTS FOR YOUR FAMILY & FRIENDS

Or you may become what is termed a 'homecrafter' and love to make products for your family and friends. For this you don't need insurance.

HOMECRAFTERS & THERAPISTS – SELLING TO THE PUBLIC

After getting feedback from family, friends or your clients, you could take the next step by creating a business and selling to the public. There are many options for selling to the public. You can open your own shop, sell from home, a web shop, at markets, arts fairs and festivals, or even host home parties. Additionally, you can easily get product and public liability insurance if you're a therapist making products or if you're a home crafter and not a therapist. See the Resources section for home craft and therapist insurers who will do this in the UK or look for home or soap crafting organisations in your own country.

POINTS TO REMEMBER WHEN SELLING YOUR SPA PRODUCTS TO THE PUBLIC

PRODUCT LABELS

If you are working within the European Union (EU), you need to:

* State the INCI (see Glossary) name on the label all of the ingredients in your products in decreasing order of volume i.e. the ingredient that takes up a greater percentage of your product is listed first.

* On the product label, you don't need to declare each essential oil in your product. You can instead use the word 'perfume', 'aroma' or 'fragrance' on the label. However, to comply with EU law, you need to identify allergens or so-called 'sensitisers' contained within the essential and fragrance oils in your products. See *Resources* section on page 132 for an easy way to deal with it.

* Ideally you need to have your full address on the product label but if you're short of space, you could get away with your telephone number, website and e-mail addresses.

* You need to include the volume or weight of product being sold and it's best to use volume (mililtres) so that you won't have to purchase an approved scale to weigh your products.

* The label also needs to state a best before date and a batch number. The batch number should enable you to trace that batch to your and your suppliers' records. The batch number can be the date that you

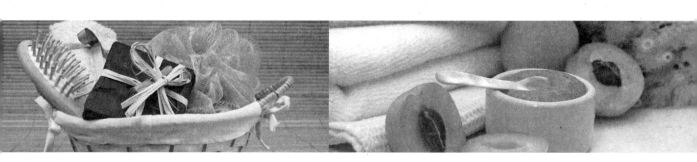

made the product e.g. if you made a product 19 July 2010, then the batch number could be 19072010. If you made different batches of products that same day you could add a number at the end e.g. 19072010-01.

MAKING YOUR PRODUCTS FOR THE PUBLIC

⚒ There are certain levels of health and hygiene standards that you need to meet.

⚒ When you make your products, you need to keep records in a book or spreadsheet, where you keep note of the recipe, who made the product, date and time of making, batch number and you need to record any incidents e.g. you had a distraction such as a phone call and you accidently put in a little bit more of a raw material than you should have done. If you are checked out by any authorities in the future or have any customer complaints, you can easily go back to your records and see if there were any irregularities. The best would be to keep a small sample of each product that you've made for the duration of its shelf life.

⚒ It is also important that you keep copies of material safety data sheets (MSDS) on every raw material that can be found on your premises. Your suppliers have to provide you with these data sheets by law, so simply request them. It's easiest to receive them on a compact disc.

⚒ To comply with the law, you need to send a sample and recipe to a cosmetic chemist or laboratory who will undertake a safety testing service for small scale producers. They will give you guidelines on how to prepare your formulation for submission to their cosmetic chemist or laboratory. This is much less expensive than you may think, See *Resources* on page 132 for the contact details for laboratory services.

It is important to say that these labelling and trading guidelines are only necessary if you sell to the public but setting up a system of good practice is an excellent habit to get into even if you're 'just' making for family and friends.

Personally, I have found that going to Trading Standards officers for help has not been helpful to me as different officers gave totally conflicting advice but of course you need to make up your own mind.

MARKETING & ADVERTISING YOUR PRODUCT

A lot of people make the mistake of not paying enough attention to marketing and advertising. The marketing and advertising you undertake should be appropriate to the size and nature of your business. In the United Kingdom, there is an extensive network of local enterprise companies who can give you advice, help draw up a business plan and may even be able to help you with small business grants. There is also a lot of information available on the web about business start up, market research, marketing, business plans and advertising.

USEFUL EQUIPMENT FOR MAKING YOUR SPA PRODUCTS

- Double-boilers or stainless steel bowls and saucepans to make double-boilers (bain-maries)
- Heat proof kitchen bowls such as stainless steel or pyrex
- Electric stick blender
- Good quality scales, preferably a gram sensitive scale one that measure to 0.1 of a gram. It depends on what you're making though, a good kitchen scale may be adequate.
- Funnels of varying sizes
- Empty glass and/or plastic jars and bottles
- Heat-proof glass measuring cylinders, jugs and beakers of varying sizes
- Measuring cups and spoons of varying sizes
- Moulds – silicone, muffin baking trays, etc
- Delbor whisk
- Spatula
- Good quality spirit-filled thermometer
- Reference book on herbs
- Reference book on essential oils

NOTE

Most of the recipes in this book are for small quantities, such as 100ml or 100g. If you want to make larger quantities, simply multiply the original quantity, by a whole number if possible.

Balancing Your Body Chemistry with Diet

Balancing the acid-alkaline chemistry in your body is of great benefit to your health and beauty and will complement your spa treatments. Balanced body chemistry is of utmost importance for the maintenance of health and correction of disease. Acidosis, or over-acidity in the body tissues, is one of the basic causes of many diseases, especially the arthritic and rheumatic diseases.

Acidity and alkalinity are measured according to the pH (potential concentration of hydrogen) scale. Water, when it has a pH of 7.0, is considered neutral - neither acid nor alkaline. Any substance with a pH below 7.0 is considered acid, becoming more acid as it approaches 1. Any substance with a pH above 7.0 is considered alkaline, becoming more alkaline up to a limit of 14.0. The body is continually striving to maintain a proper balance between acid and alkaline and this process is called homeostasis. The body makes constant adjustments in tissue and fluid pH to maintain a very narrow pH balance between 7.35 and 7.45 range in the blood. It even takes calcium from the bones in order to keep the blood alkaline.

It is not the uneaten food itself that is considered alkaline or acid, it is the product or ash of the food being 'burned' or digested in the body that is considered having an alkaline or acid effect on the body. So we can see that when food is metabolised by the body the end products are either acidic or alkaline. Acids are compounds of elements that give away hydrogen ions, alkalines are compounds of elements that attract hydrogen ions.

The body needs both acids and alkalines for its metabolism but we have more difficulty in getting rid of acid end products than alkaline end products. Also we tend to eat a diet high in acid-forming foods, particularly in countries where the western diet predominates. It is therefore easy for an accumulation of excess acids to occur in the body, which can cause us to get rheumatism or skin problems such as psoriasis. To avoid this, aim for a diet that is 70% alkaline and 30% acid.

Intercellular fluid bathes the cells and provides a means of intercellular communication, delivering materials to the cells, as well as removal of metabolic waste. When your body is too acid this intercellular fluid becomes thick and gel-like. This thickening of the intracellular fluid means that it is very difficult for waste to be expelled from the cells, as well as nutrients to enter the cells. Additionally, the acidity causes the cell membrane to become stiff, reducing cell permeability. Therefore, we must maintain the appropriate pH balance in the blood and the external cellular fluids (extracellular and intercellular fluids).

Testing Your pH

The most accurate way to test your pH is through a blood pH test but this involves a visit to your GP or specialist

blood analyst. There are, however, two ways to self-test your pH levels, either with a saliva or a urine pH test.

SALIVA TEST

To test your saliva's pH, first wait until 1 hour before, or 2 hours after, eating. Then fill up your mouth with saliva and swallow it. Then do it again. Doing this twice before testing helps to ensure that your saliva is clean and makes the test more accurate. Then the third time, put some of your saliva onto the pH paper.

Test and record your saliva pH values each day for a week before making any dietary chamges, as your pH can vary from day to day. Also make sure that you have not eaten or had a drink of anything for 2 hours before you test your saliva's pH.

Opinions vary but the general consensus seems to be that when a patient is healthy, the pH of their saliva is between the slightly alkaline 7.5 and slightly acidic 6.5 (neutral is 7.0).

URINE TEST

Urine can provide a fairly accurate picture of body chemistry, because the kidneys filter out the buffer salts of pH regulation and provide values based on what the body is eliminating.

For testing urine, let some urine flow before testing as this will give more of an average reading. Upon waking, collect a sample of your first urine midstream in a glass jar. Midstream means starting urination, stopping halfway and collecting a small sample in a glass jar and then finishing urination normally. Then tear off a small strip of pH paper strip and dip it into the urine that you've collected in the glass jar. Compare the instantaneous colour change of the paper test strip with the matching pH colour chart that comes with the strips.

Urine pH can vary from around 4.5 to 9.0 at its extremes but if your urinary pH fluctuates between 6.0 to 6.5 in the morning and between 6.5 and 7.0 in the evening, your body is functioning within a healthy range. However, opinions vary and some say that the optimal urine pH upon waking should be 7.2 or greater. I recommend that you consult a specialist practitioner to be sure.

ALKALISING YOUR DIET

One of the simplest ways to immediately create more alkalinity in your body is to regularly drink alkaline water or take supplements that increase bicarbonate levels in your blood. You can also drink so-called supergreen powdered drinks. Choose a brand that contains ingredients with high alkaline values such as spinach, broccoli, carrot, wheatgrass, barley grass, chlorella, alfalfa and sprouted grain powders. Usually the powder is simply mixed into juice or water. Alkalising supplements on the market can be taken in the same way. Another easy way to rebalance your body's pH levels is to take a bicarbonate of soda bath. See pages 37-41 for more information.

You can also rebalance your system by introducing more alkaline foods into your diet. To achieve a more alkaline diet consider replacing the acid foods in Table 1 below with alkaline alternatives in your diet.

Table 2 on page 15 lists alkaline/acid values of different foods and is based on the table that was developed by the Swedish nutritionist and Nobel Prize winner Ragnar Berg (1873-1956) in the 1930's. Berg was one of the world's top authorities on the acid-alkaline balance of foods and how this balance affects the body. His work on nutrition are still used as textbooks in many medical schools. The more -, the more acid the food is. The more +, the more alkaline. 0 is balanced. The figures represent the optimum potential of alkalinity or acidity but are not set pH values, they are more of a scale. The figures are based on eating 1 ounce, or about 28 grams, of the food.

Note: most vegetables and fruits are alkaline. All vegetable oils are neutral, neither acid nor alkaline.

TABLE 1: REPLACING ACID WITH ALKALINE PRODUCTS

ACID (TO VARYING DEGREES)	ALKALINE ALTERNATIVE
Bread – all grains except buckwheat	Sprouted grain or buckwheat bread
Grain-based pasta except buckwheat	Buckwheat-based pasta
Chocolate and cocoa drinks	Carob-based drinks
Tea, Coffee, Barley Cup	Herbal Teas
Rice or Oats Porridge	Millet or Buckwheat porridge
Meat and fish protein	Soya products e.g. Soya Beans, Firm Tofu, Textured Vegetable Protein (TVP)
Tempeh, Silken Tofu	Firm Tofu
Peanuts	Hazelnuts, Almonds
Eggs	Egg Replacer (Soya-based)
Gelatine	Agar-Agar flakes

Note: These are guidelines only. Please do your own research or consult a specialist practioner.

TABLE 2: TABLE BASED ON RAGNAR BERG'S TABLE OF ALKALINE AND ACID FOODS

ALKALINE FOODS		ACID FOODS	
Cucumber	+31	Rice with husk	-51
Dried Figs	+28	Bran	-39
Raisins	+16	Whole Wheat	-38
Dried Rose Hips	+15	Oat Flakes	-30
Tomatoes	+14	Eggs	-23
Lettuce	+14	Rye Bread	-22
Mushrooms	+13	Meat of all kinds	-10 to -24
Mandarin oranges	+12	Fish of all kinds	-10 to -19
Celery	+11	Whole Rye	-17
Oranges	+10	Cheese	-17
Carrots	+10	Cottage Cheese	-17
Lemons	+10	Peanuts	-15
Leeks	+9	Asparagus	-14
Endive	+9	Corn, polished	-14
Spinach	+9	Rice, polished	-11
Gooseberries	+9	Wheat Bread	-11
Chives	+8	Rye Crispbread	-9
Buckwheat	+8	Brussel Sprouts	-9
Millet	+8	Wheat Flour	-8
Grapes, Dried Dates	+7	Brown Beans	-8
Bananas	+7		
Potatoes, peeled	+7	Butter	-6
Blackberries	+7	Olive Oil	-6
Plums	+6	Linganberry	-6
Cabbages (all types)	+5	Corn Flour	-6
Raspberries	+5	Yellow Peas	-4
Apricots	+5	Green Beans	-4
Peaches	+5	Artichokes	-4
Blueberries	+4	Coconut flesh	-4
Pineapples	+4	Margarine	-4
Prunes	+4	Almonds, Hazelnuts	-1
Blackcurrants	+4		
Cow's Milk	+4		
Apples, Pears, Cherry	+3		
Onions	+3		
Strawberries	+2		
Melons, seedless	+2		
Sugar peas	0		

KNEIPP HYDROTHERAPY TREATMENT

... dissolve, remove and strengthen

Hydrotherapy is the use of water, either internally or externally, to restore and maintain health and to prevent disease. Modern hydrotherapy is commonly attributed to Father Sebastian Kneipp (1821-97), a Bavarian monk who believed that water can 'dissolve, remove and strengthen'. Although best known for hydrotherapy, Kneipp was a proponent of a holistic system of healing, which consists of five tenets: hydrotherapy, herbalism, exercise, nutrition, and spirituality. In this book we will only refer to one of the five, namely Kneipp hydrotherapy.

General hydrotherapy treatments include saunas, whirlpool and jacuzzi baths, steam baths, foot baths, sitz baths, and the application of cold and hot water compresses.

In this hydrotherapy section we will cover Kneipp and other therapeutic baths, which are the simplest and most basic form of spa treatments.

KNEIPP'S THEORY

- ✳ Cold water contracts the blood vessels, which leads to a decrease in the amount of blood flow. There follows a rapid return of warmth and blood.

- ✳ Warm water increases circulation and body temperature.

- ✳ Alternating with hot and cold baths works well in decongesting an area of the body.

GENERAL GUIDELINES FOR A KNEIPP BATH

1. Use a thermometer to ensure the correct temperature (check Table 3a for the appropriate temperature).

2. Do not use extreme temperatures on elderly or frail people.

3. Wait 2 hours after eating before bathing.

4. Women should not expose their bodies to extreme temperatures during menstruation.

5. Dress while wet and go to bed so that the natural body heat will be stimulated to dry your clothes. If you're very chilly after a cold bath and you're afraid of getting a cold, then rub your body with a towel, get dressed and go to bed. However, the correct therapeutic method is to dress while wet and then go to bed but please act sensibly and responsibly.

6. A cold bath could also be substituted by washing yourself with a towel dipped in ice cold water. The water should not be dried off your body – follow the instructions in guideline number 5 above.

TYPES OF KNEIPP AND THERAPEUTIC WHOLE BODY BATHS

TABLE 3A: THERAPEUTIC USES FOR DIFFERENT TEMPERATURES USED IN KNEIPP BATHS

TYPE OF KNEIPP BATH	°C	DURATION	THERAPEUTIC USE	METHOD/ PRECAUTIONS
Hot Sitz Bath	35-40°C	10-12 minutes	Good after physical training and for treating rheumatism.	Place a board over the end of the bath so that your legs can rest out of the water. Cover your legs with blankets to keep them warm.
Cool Sitz Bath	10-22°C	Soak for 1-10 minutes twice daily.	Useful for people who are not sleeping well. Also helps with bowel problems, gas, constipation, haemorrhoids, genital and urinary diseases.	As above, but with cool water.
Hot Foot Bath	7°C-40°C	Soak feet in hot water for 10-12 minutes.	Good for congestion in the upper part of the body. The heat leads the blood to the feet and helps to draw out inpurities. Good for period pains and pelvic pains, sore feet, gout, muscular and arthritic pain, bad colds, fever and headaches.	Add Epsom Salts or Bicarbonate of Soda to draw and cleanse.
Cold Foot Bath	10-18°C or less	Soak feet in water for 2-3 minutes.	Good for treating sprains and for swelling of the feet. Stimulates circulation and stimulates the whole body.	
Alternating Hot and Cold Foot Baths	Min. Hot 37°C Min. Cold 10°C	See method on right.	Good for headaches, toothache, colds, poor circulation, head and sinus congestion and foot infections.	Alternate with 3-5 minutes hot and 10 seconds cold. Always finish with cold.

TABLE 3B: THERAPEUTIC USES FOR WHOLE BODY BATHS

TYPE OF WHOLE BODY BATH	°C	DURATION	THERAPEUTIC USE	METHOD/ PRECAUTIONS
Very Hot	41-44°C	A few seconds to 1 minute	Reduces muscle pain, raises blood pressure, relaxes	
Hot	37-41°C	8-10 minutes.	Relieves pain - good for treating gout, arthritis, rheumatism	
Warm	32-37°C	10-15 minutes	Good for relaxing the system as well as for colds	Take before bedtime or in the morning
Cool 1	27-32°C	5-7 minutes	Cleansing, cools inflammations, lowers fevers	**NB** Never take a cool or cold bath if you are cold or shivering
Cool 2	16-22°C	30 seconds-2 minutes	Invigorating; improves circulation	
Cold	4-16°C	30 seconds-2 minutes	Tonic; shocks nervous system	
Very Cold	0-6°C	A few seconds under supervision	Tonic	
Alternating Hot and Cold	Min. cold 4-13°C Min. Hot 38-44°C.	See method to the right	Good for congestion, energy blockages, slow circulation	Soak for 15-30 minutes in hot then for 1 minute maximum in cold and alternate three times of each

SPA BATH TREATMENTS AND PRODUCTS

Spa Bath Treatments & Products

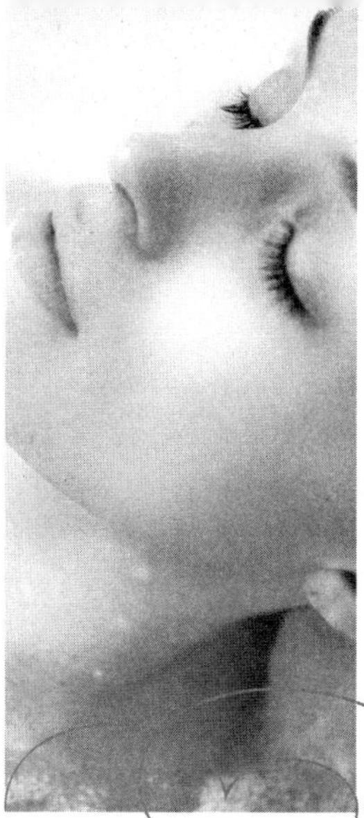

Baths & Facial Steam Baths

Bath Salts

Bath Oils

Foam Baths

Bath Melts

Bicarbonate of Soda

Bath Fizzes & Fizzy Bath Bombs

Spa bath treatments can be a very relaxing way to enjoy looking after your health and wellbeing. From simple, but effective, herbal baths to the ever-popular fizzy bath bombs, there are many ways to use healing ingredients to enjoy the benefits of spa bath treatments.

Different ways to add Herbs and Essential Oils to Baths & Facial Steam Baths

Adding herbs or essential oils to your baths or facial steam baths is super-easy and great for relaxing, healing and recharging, or for treating a specific health condition.

Recipes for Essential Oil Blends for Bath Products

The following blends of essential oils can be added directly to your ready made foam baths, turkey red oil, bath melts, fizzy bath bombs, bath salts, facial steam baths, foot, hand and whole body baths. Quantities shown in the blends below are for 100ml of whichever bath product you're adding it to and I'll refer to these recipes later in the chapter. In my experience, the optimum amount of essential oils to add to bath products is 2% of the whole amount. Adding 50 drops (2ml) of essential oils to 100ml of bath product is approximately 2%, as in the recipes below. However, in some of the recipes in the book you'll be adding 5% of essential oils to bath oils that you don't use in large quantities.

Don't put the blends directly into baths; this will mean that the essential oils will make direct contact with your skin. Add the essential oil blends to your bath products first or make up a simple bath oil by mixing the essential oil blends into the turkey red oil.

Oily skin
20 drops Lemon

12 drops Cypress

12 drops Geranium

6 drops Cedarwood

Sensitive skin
25 drops Lavender

8 drops Cedarwood

8 drops Sandalwood

8 drops Roman Chamomile

Improve circulation
20 drops Rosemary

10 drops Lavender

13 drops Pine

7 drops Juniper Berry

Anti-Rheumatism 1
Use in the evening.

25 drops Siberian Fir

7 drops Juniper Berry

10 drops Sweet Fennel

8 drops Lavender

ANTI-RHEUMATISM 2
Use in the evening.

25 drops Lavender

15 drops Clary Sage

10 drops Roman Chamomile

RHEUMATISM PAIN RELIEF

25 drops Lavender

8 drops Black Pepper

10 drops Rosemary

7 drops Juniper Berry

DETOXIFYING

8 drops Juniper Berry

8 drops Sweet Fennel

12 drops Cypress

12 drops Rosemary

10 drops Lemon

WARMING

20 drops Rosemary

8 drops Camphor

12 drops Lavender

10 drops Roman Chamomile

CHILDREN'S
From 2 years old.

30 drops Mandarin

20 drops Geranium

SLEEP WELL 1

25 drops Lavender

10 drops Ylang Ylang

10 drops Roman Chamomile

5 drops Benzoin

SLEEP WELL 2

25 drops Rosewood

10 drops Marjoram

10 drops Lavender

5 drops Bergamot

SLEEP WELL 3

25 drops Lavender

13 drops Neroli (diluted 1:9 parts in alcohol) or 2-3 drops Neroli (undiluted)

STRESS RELIEVER 1

12 drops Petitgrain

12 drops Bergamot

12 drops Ylang Ylang

12 drops Rosewood

STRESS RELIEVER 2

25 drops Ylang Ylang

17 drops Geranium

8 drops Black Pepper

REFRESHING

30 drops Lemon

8 drops Black Pepper

8 drops Geranium

4 drops Peppermint

HANGOVER RELIEF 1

Also good for headaches.

20 drops Grapefruit

15 drops Rosemary

15 drops Cedarwood

HANGOVER RELIEF 2

Also good for headaches.

13 drops Lemon

10 drops Cedarwood

10 drops Lavender

10 drops Carrot Seed

7 drops Sweet Fennel

RELAXING

30 drops Lavender

8 drops Clary Sage

4 drops Patchouli

8 drops Petitgrain

INVIGORATING

30 drops Lemon

7 drops Cedarwood Atlas

8 drops Juniper Berry

5 drops Peppermint

RECIPES FOR WHOLE BODY, FOOT AND HAND HERBAL BATH BLENDS

Here are a few suggestions for combining herbs for different applications. You can easily make up your own favourites or see Table 4 and make up a new blend.

Note: these herbal combinations only need to be infused, you don't need to make a decoction for any of them. The quantities given are for dried herbs used in a Whole Body Bath. Use half the amount of dried herbs for foot and hand baths. See glossary for definitions of 'infusions' and 'decoctions'. After the recipes I describe the different methods for using them.

For more information on the properties of herbs, please consult a trustworthy reference book.

CIRCULATION BATH

30g Rosemary leaves

20g Nettle leaves

10g Peppermint

RELAXING BATH

30g Chamomile flowers

20g Lavender flowers

10g St. John's Wort herb

ITCHY SKIN BATH

30g Chickweed herb

20g Lady's Mantle herb

10g Calendula (Marigold) flowers

ECZEMA/SKIN PROBLEMS BATH

30g Comfrey leaves

15g Plantain leaves

15g Chamomile flowers

METHODS FOR WHOLE BODY, FOOT AND HAND HERBAL BATHS

METHOD 1

The simplest way is to make a strong infusion or decoction *(see Glossary)* of herbs and allow it to stand for 20-30 minutes. Once strained, this can be added to the bath water or water you're using for your foot or hand bath. Allow your body to air dry without rinsing or towel drying and wrap up warmly after your bath.

METHOD 2

You can also place the herbs directly in the bath. This method is preferable for the use of such herbs as plantain and lady's mantle for the treatment of eczema and itchiness. When placing the herbs directly into the bath, pour 5-10 litres of boiling water over the herbs, leave for 10 minutes, before adjusting the temperature to allow the person to enter the bath. Stay in the bath for at least 20 minutes, adding more hot water if necessary in order to keep the water as hot as possible. Allow your body to air dry without rinsing or towel drying and wrap up warmly after your bath.

METHOD 3

Another method is to place fresh or dried herbs in a muslin bag, tie the bag up with string and place it in the bath. As in method 2, pour 5-10 litres of boiling water over the bag, wait ten minutes and then follow the same procedure as explained in method 2 above.

METHOD 4

To use herbs in your foam bath recipes, make a strong infusion or decoction of the herbs and strain them. Use this herbal preparation instead of the boiling water in your foam bath recipe (see page 33).

QUANTITIES OF HERBS TO USE IN HERBAL BATHS

For a whole body bath use approximately 50-100g of dried herbs or 500-1000g fresh herbs. For a foot or hand bath use 15-20g of dried herbs or 150-200g of fresh herbs. Alternatively, follow the recipes.

TIPS FOR MAKING HERBAL BATHS

* Chamomile, cleavers, lady's mantle, marigold petals, plantain, rosemary and yarrow need to be infused if using them in a recipe such as foam bath. *(See the chapter on foam baths on page 33 for the recipe and method and 'Infusion' in the Glossary for how to make an infusion.)*

* Birch and wild pansy need to be boiled for 15 minutes to extract the saponins (natural soap) in them and then strained and added to a recipe such as foam bath. See the chapter on foam baths for the recipe and method.

* Roots such as comfrey, horsetail and valerian need to be made into a decoction if using them in a recipe such as foam bath. *(See the chapter on foam baths on page 33 for the recipe and method and 'decoction' in the Glossary for how to make a decocotion.)*

* When you add herbs to a product that needs a reasonable shelf life, such as foam bath, you need to double the amount of preservative to 2 teaspoons (10ml) per litre of product. This helps remove the problems associated with naturally occurring bacteria and fungi found in dried herbs.

TABLE 4: POPULAR HERBS USED IN WHOLE BODY BATHS, FOOT BATHS, FACIAL STEAMS, AND FOAM BATH RECIPES

SINGLE HERB	CONDITION/USE
Birch leaves	For treating rheumatism, inflammations and skin problems such as weeping eczema and warts. Strengthens skin.
Calendula (Marigold) petals	Used for its healing and tissue regenerating properties for all skin types, including sensitive and babies'. Anti-inflammatory action and for treating sunburn, varicose veins, wounds, spots, acne and boils. Relieves itchiness.
Chamomile flowers	Generally soothing and relaxing. Also used for treating eczema.
Chickweed (aerial parts)	A classic herb used for soothing itchy skin and treating all kinds of skin rashes, inflammations and outbreaks.
Cleavers leaves	Purifying the blood (e.g. for psoriasis). Also used for healing wounds.
Comfrey roots	For treating eczema, skin problems, rheumatism, aches and pains. Also has anti-wrinkle and skin rejuvenating properties.
Horsetail (whole plant)	Called the 'beauty herb', it's good for strengthening connective skin and tissue. Use for treating athlete's foot and other fungal problems. Particularly good for reducing psoriasis.
Lady's Mantle (whole plant)	For soothing itchiness, skin inflammations and healing wounds, eczema and psoriasis. Good for balancing dry, sensitive, chapped or large-pored skin.
Lavender flowers	Another 'beauty herb', generally relaxing, soothing and sedative and good for treating skin rashes, inflammations, irritations, stings, etc.
Nettle leaves	Improves circulation and soothes sensitive or dry skin and eczema. Cleansing and clarifying for oily skin.
Peppermint leaves	Revitalising, clarifying and stimulating. Reduces swelling and is cooling so good for calming itchiness. Good for large-pored skin.
Plantain leaves	Excellent for treating a number of skin irritations and disorders, eg. Eczema and psoriasis.
Rosemary leaves	Warming and good for stimulating blood circulation and treating gout and joint/muscular pains. Also good for treating blackheads, spots and oily skin.
St. John's Wort herb	Its well-known calming properties are good for soothing skin irritations, inflammations, rheumatic and muscular pains. Also good for washing wounds, burns, etc.
Wild Pansy	Healing, cleansing, soothing and rejuvenating properties. Especially good for treating large-pored or problem skin, acne, psoriasis, eczema and rough skin.
Yarrow leaves	For treating haemorrhoids and varicose veins and healing sores and wounds. Relieves itchiness and used for treating eczema.

HERBAL FACIAL STEAM BATHS

Facial steam baths are an easy and enjoyable way of opening and cleansing your pores and getting your skin ready for further spa treatments. Healing herbs can be infused in the water so that their rejuvenating and nourishing benefits reach deep into your pores through the steam.

METHOD FOR HERBAL FACIAL STEAM BATHS

1. Boil water and add to a plastic, ceramic or stainless steel basin until almost full.

2. Add a few pinches of the dried herbs of your choice to the water in the basin and allow to draw for a few minutes.

3. Sit at a table with a basin of hot water and herbs in front of you. Then lean over the basin and cover your head and the basin with a large towel.

4. Keep your head at a comfortable distance above the water but so that the steam still reaches your face.

5. Sit for 5-10 minutes with your head in the 'tent' and allow the herbs and the steam to do their work.

6. Rinse your face with cool water and pat dry.

7. If not following the facial steam with another facial spa treatment, apply an astringent (see section on toners) to close the pores and finish by applying a moisturiser.

TIPS FOR HERBAL FACIAL STEAM BATHS

* Essential oils can be used instead of herbs. For ideas of which essential oils or herbs to add to your facial steam baths, see *Recipes for Essential Oil Blends for Bath products* on page 22, *Table 4: Herbs to use in Whole Body Baths, Foot Baths, Facial Steam Baths, and in Foam Bath Recipes* on page 26 and *Recipes for Herbal Bath Blends* on page 24.

* You can use the bathroom sink instead of a basin, just take a chair into the bathroom so that you can sit comfortably while taking the steam.

* For a stronger steam, you can make a boiling infusion of your chosen herb/s and fill the basin with that instead of step 2 in the method above.

BATH SALTS

Making your own bath salts is very simple and also very beneficial in spa treatments. The term 'bath salts' was created after 1900 BCE when people started to have baths in their homes. The salts release oxygen that would otherwise be bound in the water. The water then becomes saturated with oxygen, which has a deeply softening effect on the skin. The use of bath salts also cleanses the skin and draws out impurities. Bath salts can help relieve itchy and irritated skin; stimulate blood circulation; soften stiff muscles, and relieve pain. The astringent effects of the salts are also good for treating cellulite. By adding bicarbonate of soda to your bath salts, you can balance the pH level in your body. See the section on bicarbonate of soda pages 37-41.

The cheapest salt is rough sea salt but the best for healing purposes is Dead Sea salt. However, the long-term sourcing of Dead Sea salt is non-sustainable so I recommend the use of sea salt and epsom salt instead. The classic spa product, sea salt exfoliates, softens and revitalises the skin and helps to draw out toxins, relieves aches and pains, reduces stiffness after exertion, relaxes the muscles and relieves skin problems. It can be used on its own, or added to other ingredients to make bath salts, as shown in the recipes below.

BATH SALTS RECIPES

Please note that the dry ingredients in these recipes are measured in millilitres. This is easier for those who don't have accurate gram weighing scales. To measure in millilitres, simply use a kitchen measuring jug, cylinder or beaker (even for the dry ingredients, such as salt or bicarbonate of soda).

BATH SALTS BASE RECIPE 1
The turkey red oil in this recipe helps to disperse the essential oils.

Stage 1

  100ml Rough or Dead Sea Salt

Stage 2

  5ml Turkey Red Oil

  Colours (optional, see Tips for Using Bath Salts on page 30)

Stage 3

  50 drops (2ml) Essential Oils of your choice

BATH SALTS RECIPE 2
Stage 1

  100ml Epsom Salts

  100ml Rough or Dead Sea Salt

  100ml Bicarbonate of Soda

Stage 2

  50-75 (2-3ml) drops Essential Oils

Bath Salts Recipe 3
For 4-6 perfumed baths.

Stage 1
250ml Rough or Dead Sea Salt

50ml Bicarbonate of Soda

Stage 2
50-75 (2-3ml) drops of Essential Oils

Bath Salts Recipe 4
For dry or mature skin.

Stage 1
80ml Rough or Dead Sea Salt

20ml Bicarbonate of Soda

Stage 2
5ml Turkey Red Oil

10ml Macadamia Oil

3ml Thistle Oil

0.5ml/g Vitamin E Oil (undiluted)

Stage 3
15 drops Lavender Essential Oil

15 drops Geranium Essential Oil

10 drops Orange Essential Oil

2 drops Benzoin Essential Oil

Bath Salts for sensitive or acne-prone skin
Use only 2 tablespoons per bath.

Stage 1
100ml of Rough or Dead Sea Salt

Stage 2
10ml Apricot Kernel Oil

10ml Rosehip Oil

0.5ml/g Vitamin E Oil (undiluted)

Stage 3
10 drops Lavender Essential Oil

10 drops Geranium Essential Oil

5 drops Grapefruit Essential Oil

5 drops Sandalwood Essential Oil

How much of the bath salts to use

For a whole body bath, add 2-3 tablespoons to your bath.

For foot or hand baths, add 1-2 tablespoons to your bath.

General method for bath salts

1. Measure the stage 1 ingredients in a measuring jug and then pour into a bowl.

2. In a separate jug, measure and mix stage 2 together.

3. Pour stage 2 into stage 1 and stir together until everything is soaked in the salt.

4. Measure the Stage 3 ingredients, pour them into the mixture and stir well together.

5. Place the finished bath salts in a clean jar or bottle and lable.

6. The bath salts will keep for 1-2 years.

7. Add the desired amount to the bath.

8. Immerse yourself in the water for 5-20 minutes in water as hot as you can manage, without burning your skin of course!

9. Stay warm after your bath and relax quietly.

10. Make sure you drink plenty of water so that you do not become dehydrated. If you have a headache after your bath, simply drink more water.

*Add some
dried rose
petals for
that bit
of extra
luxury…*

TIPS FOR USING BATH SALTS

✳ Salt can often dry out small children's skin. Use a skin oil or moisturiser after the bath to avoid this.

✳ If you have dry skin, add some vegetable oil to the salts. It is best to add some oil to the portion of bath salts you are about to use in the bath, rather than adding it to the whole amount you have in the jar.

✳ If vegetable oils aren't added, bath salts dry out the skin and are therefore best for oily skin and acne-prone skin.

✳ When adding alkaline raw materials such as bicarbonate of soda, remember that this will soften the water, making it kinder to dry skin.

✳ When using salts in the bath, any soaps and shower gels you use at the same time will be less foamy.

✳ The best colours to use are colours that are for non-water based products. You can also use food colours, but these will fade in time. See the Glossary at the back of the book for more information about Non-Water Based Colours and the Resources section for stockists.

✳ If you find that your chosen colour is not strong enough simply add more, little by little, mixing it into the salts thoroughly until you are happy with the results.

✳ Use your favourite essential oils or see the recommended blends on page 22. If you feel you would like to increase or decrease the strength of fragrance in your products, simply adjust the amount of essential oil suggested in the recipes accordingly.

✳ Let the salt absorb the essential oils for one week before use.

✳ Add some dried rose petals for that bit of extra luxury.

✳ Drink plenty of water after a bath salts treatment and relax quietly after your bath if possible.

BATH OILS

. . . .

Estee Lauder created a 'perfume story' in the 1950's by making a very strong scented bath oil called 'Youth Dew', which was very popular amongst women. This opened the way for other American perfumes and broke the virtual monopoly of the perfume industry by the French. At that time perfumes were almost entirley sourced from France and sold in very small bottles.

There are two ways that you can make a bath oil. One way is to add essential oils to vegetable oils. The problem with this method is that the oil tends to float on the surface of the water and does not disperse easily. The oil will also tend to stick to your skin as well as to the bath.

Another way is to add essential oils to a saponified vegetable oil such as castor oil (known as turkey red oil). This helps to dissolve the essential oils, reducing the risk of skin irritations caused by the oils forming a film on the surface of the water.

If you like a bit of colour in your bath oil, add 3-6 drops of colours for non-water based products *(see 'Colours' in the Glossary)* per 100ml of bath oil.

BATH OIL RECIPES AND METHODS

Makes 100ml of bath oils.

BATH OIL RECIPE USING VEGETABLE OIL

95ml Apricot Kernel or Sweet Almond Oil (or an oil which is not too oily)

5ml Essential Oils

BATH OIL RECIPE USING VEGETABLE OIL AND GLYCERINE

Excellent for sensitive skin.

88ml Apricot Kernel Oil

8ml Glycerine or Herbal Glycerol Extract

4ml Essential Oils

METHOD FOR VEGETABLE/GLYCERINE BATH OILS

1. Measure the vegetable oil/glycerine in a bottle and add the essential oils.

2. Stir well together.

3. Shake the bottle before use.

4. Base bath oil recipes with vegetable oils and/or glycerine will keep for 1-1.5 years depending on the essential oils that you use. Citrus essential oils usually will shorten the shelf life to approximately one year but you can prolong the shelf life of your bath oil by adding 0.5ml/g undiluted vitamin E to the recipe. Do make sure that you use undiluted vitamin E oil.

HOW MUCH VEGETABLE/GLYCERINE OIL BASE BATH OIL TO USE

Use 1-2 teaspoons (5-10 ml) per whole body bath and ½ teaspoon (2-3 ml) in a foot bath.

BATH OIL RECIPE USING TURKEY RED OIL

95ml Turkey Red Oil

1 teaspoon (5ml) Essential Oils

BATH OIL RECIPE USING VODKA AND TURKEY RED OIL

60ml Turkey Red Oil

35ml Vodka

5ml Essential Oils

METHOD FOR TURKEY RED BATH OIL RECIPES

1. Add the turkey red oil to a bottle and then, if adding, the vodka and finally top up with 5ml of essential oils.

2. Stir well together.

3. Shake the bottle before use.

4. The bath oil will keep for 1.5-2 years without preservatives but, as mentioned before, including citrus essential oils in your recipes will shorten the shelf life to approximately one year.

HOW MUCH OF THE TURKEY RED BATH OILS TO USE

Use 5-10ml per whole body bath, or 2-3ml per foot bath.

FOAM BATHS

. . . .

The most effective way to use essential oils in a bath is to add them to your already-made foam bath, which acts as a dispersing agent for the oils, distributing them equally in the bath water. The water will not become oily and the essential oils will come into contact with your entire body in a safe dosage. This minimises the risk of skin irritations. You can even add vegetable oils (5-10%) to the blend if you're making your foam bath from scratch. Add the vegetable oil to the foam bath emulsifier *(see Glossary)* at the beginning of making the foam bath. Reduce water content according to how much vegetable oil you've added.

For ideas on which essential oils to add to your foam baths, see Essential Oil Blends for Bath products on page 22.

FOAM BATH RECIPE

200-250ml Foam Bath Emulsifier

750-800ml Boiling Water/or Boiling Infusion or Decoction

1 teaspoon of Preservative (use 2 teaspoons if you have replaced the boiling water with a herbal infusion or decoction)

10-20ml Essential Oils (max. 2%)

Method

1. Measure the foam bath emulsifier in a measuring jug and pour into an oven-proof bowl.

2. If adding vegetable oil, add it now.

3. Measure the boiling water from the kettle and pour that or a boiling herbal infusion or decoction into the bowl.

4. Add the preservative. See 'Preservatives' in Glossary.

5. Stir well until the mixture becomes thick.

6. Place the bowl into a basin or sink of very cold water, stirring the mixture occasionally.

7. When it has cooled to below 35°C, finally blend in your own choice of essential oils.

8. Allow the mixture to cool to room temperature, pour into bottles and label

9. Foam bath will keep for 1.5-2 years with added preservative.

HOW MUCH FOAM BATH TO USE

For a whole body bath, add 2-4 tablespoons (30-60ml) to the bath while the tap is running.

For foot or hand baths, add 1-2 tablespoons (15-30ml).

FOAM BATH TIP

⚜ When you blend in the essential oils into the foam bath mixture you will notice that the consistency can get thicker/thinner, depending on the type of essential oils you are using. If it gets too thick, add more water and preservative, generally 1 drop of preservative for every 10ml of water you add. When you next make the foam bath, simply adjust the quantities accordingly. If it gets too thin, add more emulsifier.

BATH MELTS

. . . .

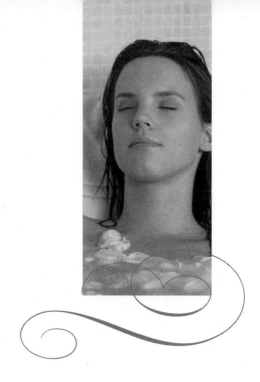

Bath melts are a novel way to add healing and rejuvenating ingredients to your bath. They are easy to make and fun to use. They are also so easy to sell at local markets and fairs. Just pop them into small plastic or cellophane bags with shredded paper or wrap them in coloured cellophane tied together with a colourful ribbon, and you have a bestseller! For ideas on which essential oils to use in your bath melt recipes, see page 22 for Recipes for Essential Oil Blends for Bath products.

BATH MELT RECIPES

Recipes make 100g.

RELAXING BATH MELT
This bath melt is not only relaxing, but very soothing and healing for dry or inflamed skin.

Stage 1
   65g Cocoa Butter

Stage 2
   32g Foam Bath Emulsifier

Stage 3
   2-3 drops Blue Azulene Colour *(see Glossary)*

   1ml/g Bisabolol

   50 drops/2ml/2% Lavender Essential Oil

BATH MELT FOR DRY/MATURE SKIN
Very nourishing to your skin, this bath melt is also excellent for chapped or problem skin.

Stage 1
   60g Cocoa Butter

   10g Mango Butter

Stage 2
   25g Foam Bath Emulsifier

Stage 3
   2ml/g Vitamin E Oil (undiluted)

   50 drops/2ml/2% Essential Oils

BATH MELT FOR SENSITIVE SKIN
Perfect for sensitive skin, this bath melt is rich in vitamins and healing ingredients.

Stage 1
   64g Cocoa Butter

   5g Apricot Kernel Oil

Stage 2
   24g Foam Bath Emulsifier

Stage 3
   1ml/g Vitamin E Oil (undiluted)

   1ml/g Bisabolol

2ml/g Rosehip Seed CO_2 Extract

1ml/g Calendula CO_2 Extract

50 drops/2ml/2% Essential Oils

ANTI-WRINKLE BATH MELTS

Healing and rejuvenating for your skin, the name says it all!

Stage 1

64g Cocoa Butter

Stage 2

25g Foam Bath Emulsifier

Stage 3

5ml/g Vitamin E Oil (undiluted)

2ml/g Sea Buckthorn Pulp CO_2 Extract

2ml/g Remodelling Intense

50 drops/2ml/2% Essential Oils

BATH MELTS FOR BLACK SKIN

A highly nutritious and vitamin-rich bath melt well suited to black skin. Makes 100g of bath melts.

Stage 1

65g Cocoa Butter

10g Avocado Butter

Stage 2

20g Foam Bath Emulsifier

Stage 3

2ml/g Vitamin E Oil (undiluted)

1ml/g Carrot CO_2 Extract

50 drops/2ml/2% Essential Oils

BASE BATH MELT RECIPE WITH BETAINE DETERGENT

Betaine detergent is the milder choice of foaming agent so is more suitable for sensitive skin. **Note***: the use of betaine detergent makes the consistency of bath melts like soft, chewy toffee, which makes it much more difficult to get out of a mould tray. To avoid this, why not pour the mixture into individual paper muffin moulds. The paper can then be peeled away when using the bath melt.*

Stage 1

65g Cocoa Butter

Stage 2

33g Betaine Detergent

Stage 3

50 drops/2ml/2% Essential Oils

GENERAL METHOD FOR MAKING BATH MELTS

1. Place the butters/vegetable oils in a double boiler (bain-marie) and melt.

2. Cool down the butters/oils mixture by replacing the hot water in the bottom of the bain-marie/double boiler with very cold water. Stir the mixture in the upper saucepan until the mixture thickens around the edge to the consistency of a thin soup. Stir occasionally as it cools.

3. Immediately pour in the pre-measured stage 2 ingredients and blend together with a spoon until fully blended.

4. Immediately add the pre-measured stage 3 ingredients and stir well. Do not allow to thicken too much, it should still be pourable.

5. Pour the mixture quickly into a muffin mould tray or individual paper muffin cases.

6. Put the muffin mould tray (or filled muffin cases on a flat tray) in a fridge until the bath melts are hard or leave to harden overnight outside of the fridge, say on the kitchen table.

7. If using a mould tray: once hardened, simply turn the mould upside down and press with your fingers on the back of the mould so that the melts fall out. If they don't fall out by themselves, knock the mould tray against the table and they'll usually fall out.

HOW MANY BATH MELTS TO USE

Use 1 bath melt for a whole body bath and ½ bath melt for a foot bath.

TIPS FOR BATH MELTS SUCCESS

※ Always cool the butters/vegetable oils down after you have melted them and before you add stage 2 ingredients, otherwise the bath melt will disintegrate when you remove the melts from the moulds. If the melts do disintegrate, remelt the pieces and repeat the procedure.

※ For that extra luxury, you could try adding melted chocolate to the mould before adding your mixture. Looks good; smells good...

※ For variation and different properties, add clay, spices, oats, carotene, bisabolol, blue azulene, vitamins, vegetable oils and dried calendula or rose petals.

※ Wrap your bath melts around a fizzy bath bomb (see pages 40-41 for recipes and method) for a spectacular effect.

※ If you are unhappy with your finished bath melts, simply remelt them and add a little more essential oil.

※ If the blend of butters/vegetable oils and emulsifier is too hot when you pour it into the moulds they can become soft and liquid inside. Re-melt them or place in the freezer for 1 hour.

※ If you cannot get the melts out of the moulds, then you have most likely poured the mixture into the moulds when it was too hot. Simply put them in the freezer for 1 hour and then try to remove them again.

※ Don't use moulds with intricate details, as they are more likely to crack.

※ If you pour 100g of bath melt mixture into muffin moulds that you can buy in the baking section in cook shops, 99p shops or supermarkets, you will make approximately 4-5 small individual bath melts.

※. Store your melts in a sealed food-grade plastic bag or airtight container in a cool, dark place away from heat and light.

BICARBONATE OF SODA

Also known as baking soda, bread soda or sodium bicarbonate, bicarbonate of soda is a soluble white crystalline chemical compound, with a slight alkaline taste. It is found in many mineral springs and also produced artificially. In making spa products it is used for its alkalising properties in baths and bath salts and to make fizzy bath bombs and in baths and bath salts.

Adding bicarbonate of soda to your bath is good for restoring your alkaline/acid balance. Bathing 1-2 times per week will draw out the excess acidity from your body. It is also excellent for people prone to muscle pain, rheumatism, eczema and psoriasis, who need to restore their acid/alkaline balance, otherwise these conditions are hard to heal. Always start with smaller amounts to determine the body's reaction and gradually add more bicarbonate of soda to your baths. Bicarbonate of soda also soothes itchy or sunburnt skin and increases circulation in the body.

Here we look at 3 ways to add Bicarbonate of Soda to your Baths:

1. Bicarbonate of Soda powder
2. Bath Fizzes
3. Fizzy Bath Bombs

BICARBONATE OF SODA POWDER RECIPES

Adding bicarbonate of soda to foot, hand or whole body baths is a simple and inexpensive way to enjoy the benefits of this alkalising substance.

FOR WHOLE BODY BATHS

Start with 1-2 tablespoons of bicarbonate of soda and increase this up to 5 tablespoons. On alternate nights take a relaxing chamomile bath (see page 25).

FOR FOOT OR HAND BATHS

Generally 1-2 tablespoons bicarbonate of soda but for more information see the Foot products section on pages 43-53.

FOR HAND BATHS

1 tablespoon bicarbonate of soda.

TIPS FOR ALL BICARBONATE OF SODA-BASED BATHS

- ✳ Add the correct amount of bicarbonate of soda to your bath.

- ✳ Immerse your body, feet, or hands in water as hot as you can manage. Be careful not to burn your skin though.

- ✳ After your bath, do not dry with a towel; air dry instead.

- ✳ After a foot bath, stay warm and put on warm woollen socks on your wet feet and leave on for between half an hour to an hour.

- ✳ After your bicarbonate of soda bath it would be ideal to rest, go to sleep or engage in a quietly relaxing activity.

- ✳ Make sure you drink plenty of water so that you do not become dehydrated. If you have a headache the morning after your bath, simply drink more water.

- ✳ People with heart problems should not take high dosage sodium bicarbonate baths.

BATH FIZZES & FIZZY BATH BOMBS

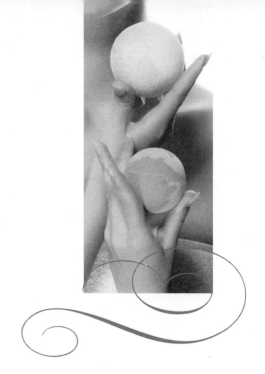

These products are fun and easy to make. It is easy to add essential oils and dried flowers to create your own unique product. If you want to package them with style, why not try wrapping the bath bombs in small plastic bags with shredded paper, or in coloured cellophane tied together with a colourful ribbon or store the fizzes in coloured glass jars. They both make popular and colourful gifts and sell well at fairs and markets.

COMMON TIPS FOR MAKING BATH FIZZES AND FIZZY BATH BOMBS

✱ You can add dried flower petals, such as rose, marigold, lavender, etc, to your mixture at the end. You can also add different spices, such as powdered ginger, mustard, cloves, cinnamon, etc.

✱ If you use water-based colours (such as food colourings), your mixture will start to fizz as you mix the ingredients. Even glycerine contains some water, so it is best to use propylene glycol-based or pearlescent colours. See Glossary and Resources sections.

✱ Keep the bath bombs and bath fizz mixture dry by storing them in a sealed container and don't store in a humid area (like the bathroom).

✱ If you make a lot of fizzy bath bombs or bath fizzes, use rubber or latex gloves as too much citric acid can irritate the skin.

BATH FIZZES RECIPES

Easy to make and store in a jar. One of the spa recipes you can start with straight away at home with simple ingredients you can buy from super-markets and the corner pharmacy. Bath fizzes have real health benefits.

Your bath fizz mixture will keep for 1.5-2 years.

BASE RECIPE FOR BATH FIZZ 1
Makes 100g of Bath Fizz, enough for 1-2 Whole Body Baths.

75g Sodium Bicarbonate

25g Citric Acid (you can buy it from any pharmacy)

Method

Mix the ingredients together and store in a glass jar or gift-wrap in a cellophane bag.

BASE RECIPE FOR BATH FIZZ 2
Makes 100g of Bath Fizz, enough for 1-2 Whole Body Baths.

Stage 1

58g Sodium Bicarbonate

30g Citric Acid

10g Cornflour or potato flour

Stage 2

1-2ml/g of Pearlescent Colours OR 1ml/g of Non-Water Based Colour

Add approximately 20 drops of Essential Oils

Method

1. Mix the ingredients in stage 1 together in a mixing bowl or ice cream container.

2. Add the measured colours and essential oils to the mixture and blend it well together.

3. Break up white lumps with your fingers.

4. Store in a glass jar or gift-wrap in a cellophane bag.

HOW MUCH BATH FIZZ TO USE FOR A WHOLE BODY BATH

If you have very sensitive skin, start by adding 2 tablespoons, gradually working up to 5 tablespoons over a period of 3 weeks. Otherwise, generally 5 tablespoons per bath is safe.

METHOD FOR MAKING AND USING BATH FIZZES IN WHOLE BODY BATHS

1. Follow the instructions for making the bath fizz under each bath fizz recipe.

2. Put the appropriate amount of bath fizz in hot bath water that has a temperature between 28 and 35°C.

3. Soak in the bath for at least between 10 and 20 minutes but you can stay in for up to 30 minutes. Lie very still and your body will get covered with tiny carbon dioxide bubbles, which helps to insulate the body from lowering temperatures.

4. Don't shower after the bath and don't dry with a towel. Allow your body to air-dry in the warmth and rest for 1-2 hours afterwards.

HOW MUCH OF THE BATH FIZZ TO USE FOR HAND AND FOOT BATHS

Use 1-2 tablespoons of the 'Base Recipe (1 or 2) for Bath Fizz'.

METHOD FOR MAKING AND USING BATH FIZZES IN FOOT AND HAND BATHS

1. Follow the instructions for making the bath fizz under each bath fizz recipe.

2. Put the appropriate amount of bath fizz into a foot or hand basin that contains water between 28 and 35°C.

3. Immerse your hands or feet in the bath for 5-15 minutes.

4. Don't dry with a towel. Allow your hands to air dry in the warmth, or put socks on your wet feet and rest for 1-2 hours afterwards.

TIPS FOR MAKING BATH FIZZES

* When using corn flour or potato flour to your blend, you can use water-based colours. First colour the flour and allow to dry completely before adding the other powders.

* You can also use other types of powders as moisture-absorbing products (such as talc, sea salt, icing sugar, etc). Use 10-15%. These powders will stop the sodium bicarbonate and citric acid from reacting with each other before they come into contact with the water.

✳ When mixing the powders it is a good idea to use surgical gloves to avoid possible skin irritation.

Fizzy Bath Bomb Recipes

Because fizzy bath bombs are such an exciting and popular product in the marketplace today, we may be excused for thinking that they're something new. But they're not; European resorts and spas have been making fizzy bath bombs for at least 100 years! The spas injected liquid carbon dioxide gas into the thermal waters and called the jets of gas *carbon dioxide bombs.* They also pressed bicarbonate of soda together with citric acid and called them *bath tablets* or *bath balls.*

Citrus Bomb
Makes 200g of bath bomb mixture, enough for up to 10 bombs.

Stage 1

120g Bicarbonate of Soda

60g Citric Acid and Cellulose (*See Glossary*)

4 teaspoons finely cut organic, unwaxed lemon peel

Stage 2

15g Cocoa Butter

13g Turkey Red Oil

Stage 3

2ml/g Yellow Non-Water Based Colour

50-75 drops (2-3ml) Lemon Essential Oil

Dry Skin Bomb
Makes 200g of bath bomb mixture, enough for up to 10 bombs.

Stage 1

120g Bicarbonate of Soda

60g Citric Acid and Cellulose

Stage 2

15g Shea Butter

10g Turkey Red Oil

10ml Borage Oil

1ml/g Vitamin E Oil (undiluted)

Stage 3

50-75 drops (2-3ml) Essential Oils of your choice

HOW MANY FIZZY BATH BOMBS TO USE

For a whole body bath, use 1-2x 20g fizzy bath bombs.

For a hand or foot bath, use 1x 20g fizzy bath bombs.

METHOD FOR MAKING FIZZY BATH BOMBS

1. Mix the Stage 1 ingredients together in a kitchen bowl or ice cream container.

2. Melt Stage 2 ingredients together, (first the fats or oils and then the turkey red oil) in a double boiler (a saucepan, pyrex bowl or stainless steel bowl immersed in a larger saucepan of water).

3. Measure the essential oils in a measuring spoon or cylinder or by counting out the drops. 1ml=20-25 drops.

4. Blend stage 2 ingredients and stage 3 essential oils into stage 1 and knead the mixture as you would dough.

5. Add the colour (if using any) from stage 3 to the mixture little by little until you are happy with the colour.

6. Form the bombs with your hands* and leave them to dry on waxed paper or press them into paper or

Lemon Essential Oil is perfect for your Citrus Bomb…

aluminium muffin cases. Allow to dry out overnight. *Make sure that you protect your hands with gloves if you have sensitive skin or you're making a lot of them.*

TIPS FOR MAKING FIZZY BATH BOMBS

※ I recommend forming the bombs with your hands, or using paper or aluminium foil muffin moulds easily available in shops when following the recipes in this book. This is because it is trickier and more difficult to use especially designed plastic moulds as it is harder to get the bombs out of these types of moulds.

※ If you want to use two types of essential oils and colours for each half of the bomb, mix them separately and join the two halves together at the end.

※ Keep the bath bombs dry by storing them in a plastic lunch box and don't store in a humid area (like the bathroom).

※ Bath bombs can be used as air fresheners prior to use in the bath. Simply put them in the bathroom. As the fragrance dissipates, add them to the bath water. The warm water will rejuvenate the potency of the fragrance.

※ Be creative with your wrapping and packaging. Shredded paper and coloured cellophane with coloured ribbon can help to make this a unique and fun product if giving as a gift or selling them.

※ Approximately 200g of the fizzy bath bomb mixture can make up to 10x20g fizzy bath bombs.

FOOT PRODUCTS

FOOT PRODUCTS

FOOT BATHS

FOOT GELS

FOOT OINTMENTS

SPECIAL FOOT TREATMENTS

Most of us take our feet for granted. How many times a day do we stop to give our feet a rest or a rub? That's why most people just love to have their feet massaged or to give their feet a treat. And, as the whole body is reflected in the feet, when the feet are being looked after, so is the whole person.

But sometimes the feet need more than just a treat. Cracked feet, dry feet, sweaty feet, swollen feet or feet with fungus problems all need special attention. That's the reason I've included a lot of recipes to encourage healthy feet.

FOOT BATHS

. . . .

Foot baths were more popular before we had bathtubs and there was less hot water readily available. Toxins accumulate in the feet as they pass through the bloodstream and health is directly related to the feet, as they contain nerve endings corresponding to each part of the body. A lot of cleansing takes place in the feet, so we tend to get a lot of problems with our feet, for instance, fungal infections and pains. To cleanse your whole body, you can take a foot bath every day to remove harmful toxins and flush out impurities, assisting the body's natural detoxification process.

GENERAL GUIDANCE FOR FOOT BATHS

Never use the same foot bath recipe for two days in a row. It is best to interchange recipes. The only exception to this rule is using only sodium bicarbonate or an infusion of Roman chamomile flowers. In this case you can use these treatments for up to a week before you change to another treatment.

BASIC FOOT BATH RECIPE

RECIPE AND METHOD

1. Fill a basin with 5-6 litres of water heated to around 40°C.

2. Immerse your feet for 15-20 minutes.

3. Dry with a towel.

4. Keep your feet warm afterwards.

This is the most simple type of foot bath but you can add other active ingredients to treat specific problems.

... assisting the body's natural detoxification process

ADDITIONAL INGREDIENTS TO ADD TO THE BASIC FOOT BATH

Use one of the ingredients or combine them e.g. you can add up to 100g of salt such as rough sea salt, Dead Sea salt or Epsom salt, as well as adding essential oils. For more ideas, see the Foot Bath Recipes on page 45 and Recipes for Essential Oil Blends for Bath products on page 22.

ESSENTIAL OILS ON THEIR OWN

Add a maximum of 6 drops per bath.

ESSENTIAL OILS IN A CARRIER OIL

Add 5ml of essential oils (100-125 drops) to 95ml vegetable oil or turkey red oil (see Glossary). Mix well and then use ½ teaspoon per foot bath.

ESSENTIAL OILS IN A BASE FOAM BATH

Add 2ml (50 drops) of essential oils to 100ml of base foam bath *(see page 33)*. Use 1-1½ teaspoons in your foot bath.

BICARBONATE OF SODA

Add 1-2 tablespoons per bath.

ROUGH SEA SALT/DEAD SEA SALT/ EPSOM SALT

Add up to 100g to your bath.

HERBAL INFUSIONS OR DECOCTIONS

Add a strong infusion or decoction (see Glossary) of herbs and add directly to the foot bath.

FOOT BATH RECIPES

HERBAL FOOT BATH RECIPES

SLEEP WELL 1
5g Hops

5g Chamomile flowers

5g Lavender flowers

SLEEP WELL 2
10g Chamomile flowers

5g Lavender flowers

Method for Sleep Well foot baths

1. Make an infusion for 10-15 minutes in hot water.

2. Then adjust the temperature to around 40°C by adding cold water to the basin.

3. Don't strain off the flowers.

4. Immerse your feet in the basin.

CIRCULATION HERBAL FOOT BATH 1
Make a decoction of:

7g Rosemary leaves

7g Birch leaves

CIRCULATION BATH 2
2g Ginger, finely cut

2g Cloves, whole

8g Yarrow flowers

Method

1. Cut the ginger finely into thin slices.

2. Boil the ginger and cloves for 20 minutes.

3. Then add 8g yarrow flowers and let everything infuse for another 10 minutes.

4. Immerse your feet in the basin.

ESSENTIAL OIL FOOT BATH RECIPES

Simply add these essential oil blends and other liquid ingredients to your basic hot water foot bath.

SWOLLEN FEET
2 drops Juniper Berry Essential Oil

2 drops Lavender Essential Oil

1 drop Cypress Essential Oil

1 teaspoon Arnica Tincture

1 teaspoon Apple Cider Vinegar

TIRED FEET
1 drop Juniper Berry Essential Oil

2 drops Peppermint Essential Oil

1 drop Rosemary Essential Oil

HEAVY FEET
2 drops Lemon Essential Oil

2 drops Cypress Essential Oil

1 drop Rosemary Essential Oil

WARM FEET
2 drops Eucalyptus Essential Oil

2 drops Peppermint Essential Oil

1 drop Lavender Essential Oil

COLD FEET

2 drops Rosemary Essential Oil

1 drop Ginger Essential Oil

1 drop Black Pepper Essential Oil

ATHLETE'S FOOT

4 drops Tea Tree Essential Oil

1 drop Lavender Essential Oil

1 drop Myrrh Essential Oil

RELAXING FOOT BATH

3 drops Lavender Essential Oil

1 drop Ylang Ylang Essential Oil

1 drop Roman Chamomile Essential Oil

OTHER FOOT BATH RECIPES

Unless otherwise stated the method for making these foot baths is to simply dissolve the ingredients in your basic hot water foot bath.

FOOT BATH FOR HARD SKIN 1

To soften and moisturise the feet.

3 drops Myrrh Essential Oil

30g Carbamide crystals (stir into foot bath to make sure that they are dissolved)

10ml Lactic Acid

FOOT BATH FOR HARD SKIN 2

2 tablespoon of Sea Salt

2 tablespoons of Sodium Bicarbonate

1 tablespoon of Citric Acid

10g of Honey (it is moisturising)

FOOT BATH FOR SWOLLEN FEET

This is a commercial foot bath product that you can package and sell.

100ml Base Foam Bath (see page 33 for recipe)

2ml Arnica Tincture

18 drops Lavender Essential Oil

15 drops Tea Tree Essential Oil

12 drops Juniper Essential Oil

4 drops Peppermint Essential Oil

SALT FOOT BATH

This is a commercial foot bath product that you can package and sell. Tip: to make it an even better commercial product, add pearlescent colour to the salt.

Stage 1

100g Rough/Epsom/Dead Sea Salt

Stage 2

50 drops (2ml) of Essential Oils of your choice

Approximately 1ml Pearlescent Colour (optional)

Method

1. Stir the essential oils into the salt, making sure there is an even distribution of the oils.

2. If adding pearlescent colour, then stir in the colour to the salt/ essential oil little by little until you are happy with the colour.

3. Place in a jar and close the lid firmly. If adding colour, place in transparent or semi-transparent jar to show off the colour.

4. Ideally let it stand for 1 week before using.

ACIDITY REDUCTION FOOT BATH

This draws out acidity from your whole body and is very good for people with arthritis, rheumatism and muscular or back pain.

1-3 tablespoons of Bicarbonate of Soda

Method

1. Add the bicarbonate of soda to the hot water (40°C).

2. Immerse your feet for 10-20 minutes.

3. Don't dry your feet. Instead put on warm woollen socks and leave on for 30-60 minutes while relaxing.

NB *Start this foot bath treatment with 1 tablespoon of sodium bicarbonate and increase to 3 tablespoons over a period of 3 weeks. For the first week use one tablespoon, the second week you can increase it to 2 tablespoons and the third week, use three tablespoons.*

FOOT GELS

. . . .

It is very easy to make a gel for different foot problems and conditions. Gels are also very handy, being easy to apply as well as being quickly absorbed into the skin. Here we make a base gel, to which essential oils can be added for various foot treatments. We add aloe vera concentrate for its pain relieving, antiseptic and healing properties. The recipe refers to a 1:9 aloe vera liquid concentrate. Apart from using it to make aloe vera gel, you can also add the concentrated aloe vera directly to your creams, lotions, etc. Aloe vera binds moisture to the skin and is cooling and beneficial to all types of skin problems. The base gel, once made, is versatile and can also be used to help heal wounds, burns, cuts, grazes, sunburn, psoriasis, eczema, acne, and to minimise scar tissue from wounds, burns, etc. You can make up a big batch of the gel by multiplying the amounts in the recipe. You can also tailor make smaller batches for different conditions and uses by mixing extra ingredients to the already-made base gel.

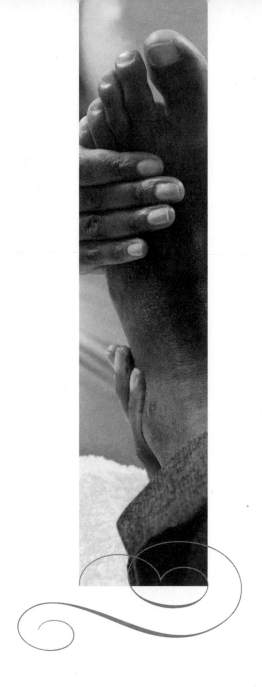

BASE ALOE VERA GEL RECIPE
Makes 100ml.

Stage 1

89ml Spring Water

2ml/1g/ ½ teaspoon Xanthan Gum

Stage 2

10ml Aloe Vera Concentrate

10 drops Preservative

Method

Stage 1

1. Measure the water in a jug and pour into a bowl.

Use healing Aloe Vera concentrate to make your base gel…

2. Fill a 2ml measuring spoon with xanthan gum powder and level with a straight knife edge.

3. Sprinkle the xanthan gum powder over the water little by little, whisking vigorously. If your gel gets lumpy, blend until smooth with an electric blender.

4. When there are no more lumps, stop whisking or blending.

Stage 2

1. Add all of the other pre-measured ingredients and mix well in to the gel.

FOOT GEL RECIPES

'SMELLY FEET' GEL
Tea tree essential oil has been scientifically proven to alleviate the problem of smelly feet. Makes approximately 100ml.

100ml/g Base Aloe Vera Gel

30 drops Tea Tree Essential Oil

10 drops Lavender Essential Oil

3 drops Peppermint Essential Oil

5 drops Lemon Essential Oil

'SWOLLEN FEET' GEL
Makes approximately 100ml.

100ml/g Base Aloe Vera Gel

5ml Arnica Tincture

10 drops Lavender Essential Oil

10 drops Fragonia Essential Oil

5 drops Juniper Essential Oil

3 drops Peppermint Essential Oil

3 drops Rosemary Essential Oil

TIPS FOR MAKING FOOT GELS

- If you prefer your gel to have a thicker consistency, sprinkle more xanthan gum, little by little, into the finished gel until you get the consistency you want. Remember to make the gel of a pourable consistency if you want to bottle it.

- Don't whisk the xanthan gum and water so much that the mixture becomes white. Only whisk it enough to remove the lumps.

- If you use the gels every day, they dry out your skin. Add 1-3 % vegetable oil to the already-made gel to counter this.

FOOT OINTMENTS

Ointments are very easy to make and are very good for treating foot conditions and for softening and protecting the feet in general.

FOOT OINTMENT RECIPES

Makes approximately 100ml/g.

FOOT OINTMENT 1

Excellent for healing cracked or dry skin.

Stage 1

15g Beeswax

18ml Jojoba Oil

60ml Olive Oil

Stage 2

5ml Calendula Tincture/Calendula Oil

0.5ml/g Vitamin E Oil (undiluted)

Stage 3

25 drops/1ml Lavender Essential Oil

25 drops/1ml Myrrh Essential Oil

FOOT OINTMENT 2

Excellent for healing chapped or inflamed skin or wounds.

Stage 1

15g Beeswax

50ml Calendula Oil

Stage 2

16ml Thistle Oil

16ml Comfrey Oil

... soften and protect your feet...

Stage 3

25 drops/1ml Essential Oils

2ml/g Vitamin E Oil (undiluted)

METHOD FOR MAKING FOOT OINTMENTS

1. Melt the stage 1 ingredients together in a double boiler.

2. When they are completely melted, remove the bowl or saucepan from the double boiler.

3. Add pre-measured stage 2 ingredients to the bowl or saucepan.

4. While still in the original bowl, whisk the ointment until it has cooled to a consistency of a thick soup and then thoroughly mix in pre-measured stage 3 ingredients.

5. Pour into jars.

TREATMENTS FOR SPECIAL FOOT CONDITIONS

ATHLETE'S FOOT

Athlete's foot is characterised by moist, red or peeling skin and itchiness between the toes. Even the heels and soles of the feet can be covered in white peeling skin. The skin often becomes cracked and can be painful. Athlete's foot is a fungal infection of the foot caused by *Tinea pedis* and is highly contagious. It can be contracted at sports facilties, swimming pools and schools.

DIFFERENT TREATMENT METHODS FOR ATHLETE'S FOOT

Always add a little lavender essential oil to tea tree products and treatments as the two oils have a synergistic effect.

UNDILUTED TEA TREE ESSENTIAL OIL

Apply 3-4 drops of undiluted tea tree essential oil morning and evening for approximately 2 weeks. Finish the treatment by applying a tea tree cream or ointment for 2 weeks after the athlete's foot has cleared.

FOOT BATH

Take a foot bath 1-5 times per week using either epsom salts (1 tablespoon to a basin of water) or the blend 'Foot Bath for Athlete's Foot' on page 46 (1-2 teaspoons to a basin of water). After the foot bath, rub tea tree cream onto your feet. Add 2-3ml of tea tree essential oil plus 10-15 drops of lavender essential oil into 100ml of base cream (see page 106 for details or use your already-made own base cream) onto the affected areas afterwards.

WHOLE BODY BATH

Take regular whole body baths with 8-10 drops of tea tree oil added to bath water mixed into a small amount of vegetable oil or turkey red bath oil or you can even use tea tree shampoo.

COMPRESS

Apply a tea tree compress to affected areas: mix together 4% tea tree essential oil plus 1% lavender essential oil into 95% olive or other vegetable oil. Soak a piece of cotton cloth in the mixture and wrap around the foot, making sure that the affected area is covered. Cover with clingfilm and finally cover everything with a cotton sock. Sleep with this on overnight. In the morning wash feet and continue other treatments also.

SWEATY OR SMELLY FEET

Sweaty or smelly feet are usually caused by socks or stockings which are either dirty, or too tight or too warm, or by unwashed feet. Research carried out by Morten Walker, in April 1972 indicated that 58 out of 60 patients got rid of their sweaty feet problems through using tea tree essential oil. The report,

published in 1972 in *Current Podiatry*, 'Clinical Investigation of Australian Melaleuca Alternifolia oil for a variety of common foot problems', describes the treatment with postive results of foot problems such as athlete's foot, post-operative removal of toenails, cracked skin caused by fungal and other infections, infected corns, hammertoe, deep cracks and nail infections (paronychia).

Different Methods of Treatments for Smelly or Sweaty Feet

ALOE VERA GEL

Wash feet and rub in aloe vera tea tree gel. See the recipe for 100ml aloe vera gel under 'Foot Gels' on page 48 and add 2-4ml of tea tree essential oil plus 15 drops of lavender essential oil either at the final stage of making the gel or mix these oils in thoroughly to an already-made base gel.

FOOT BATHS

Try the Recipes below.

Antiseptic Foot Bath 1

15-20 drops of Tea Tree Essential Oil

2 drops of Peppermint Essential Oil

2 drops of Lavender Essential Oil.

Antiseptic Foot Bath 2

100ml Base Foam Bath (see page 33 for recipe)

25 drops Tea Tree Essential Oil

15 drops Lavender Essential Oil

7 drops Lemon Essential Oil

3 drops Peppermint Essential Oil

ANTISEPTIC FOOT SPRAY

After any of the above treatments, spray your feet with an antiseptic foot spray, such as this one:

Recipe for Antiseptic Foot Spray

This will keep for 1 year without any preservatives. Makes approximately 100ml.

100ml Still Spring Water

40 drops/1.5ml of Tea Tree Essential Oil

20-30 drops of Fragonia Essential Oil

10 drops of Lavender Essential Oil

Method

1. Measure the ingredients and blend in a bottle with a spray cap.

2. Always shake before use because essential oils do not dissolve in water.

3. Spray your feet morning and evening.

EXTRA TIPS FOR TREATING SMELLY OR SWEATY FEET

1. Wash your feet every day, drying them properly, particularily between the toes. If the skin is very sensitive or fragile, use a hairdryer instead of a towel.

2. Avoid public pools, if you possibly can.

3. Do not wear wellington boots or shoes with tight laces. Change socks or stockings every day and wear shoes which breathe.

4. Kill the fungus in your shoes by putting your shoes in a plastic bag into your freezer overnight or by placing your shoes outside during the winter when temperatures are below freezing.

5. Kill the fungus in your socks or stockings by adding 20-30 drops of tea tree essential oil to the rinse cycle compartment of your washing machine or, if handwashing, presoak the socks in water that has tea tree essential oil added to it.

6. Rub the inside of your shoes with kitchen paper that has tea tree essential oil sprinkled onto it.

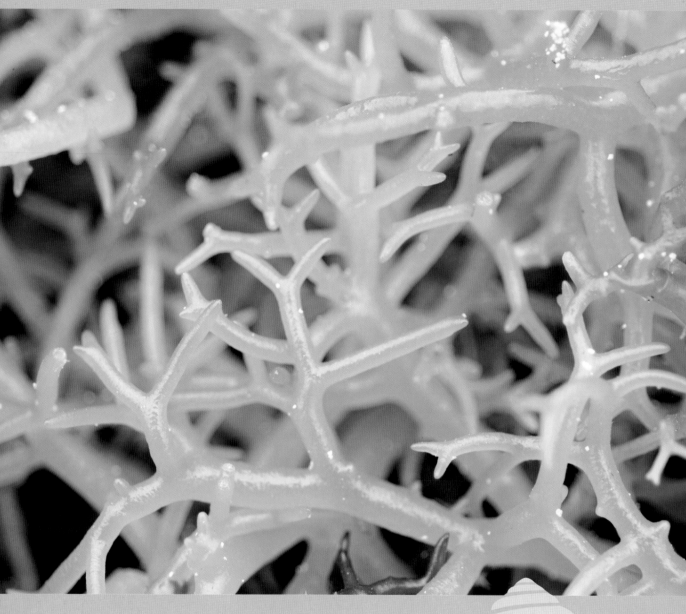

SEAWEED
TREATMENTS

SEAWEED TREATMENTS

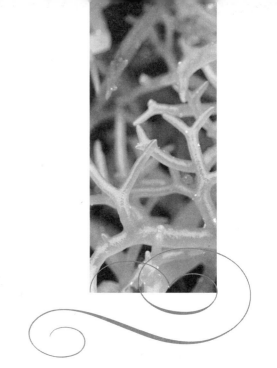

CARRAGEEN & SEAWEED BATHS

SEAWEED & SALT BATHS

SEAWEED BODY WRAP

ACTIVE HEATING MARINE MUD

Seaweed products have long been used by humans for food and healing. They are becoming increasingly popular for use as spa and thalassotherapy products. *Thalassa* is Greek for "sea" and lends its name to this unique method of preventative and curative treatment which uses the renowned therapeutic virtues of seawater and seaweed to oxygenate, tone, moisturise and revitalise the body and the skin. Different types of seaweed are used for different therapeutic effects.

Certain types of seaweed are rich in protein and the protein found in these plants typically contain all eight essential amino acids. Many marine algae are a source of vitamin B_{12}, which is rarely found in land vegetables. The potassium/sodium content of sea vegetables is usually quite close to that occurring naturally in the human body. The minerals and vitamins, which they contain are in a form which can easily be assimilated.

All types of seaweed stimulate the blood circulation, soften tight muscles and soothe the pain associated with skin irritation and sunburn. When buying seaweeds for baths it is easiest to get carrageen, kombu, wakame or funori. The last three are seaweeds that are found in Japan.

CARRAGEEN & SEAWEED BATHS

CARRAGEEN

Carrageen is a dark purple edible seaweed (algae), also known as Irish Moss, found on the rocky north Atlantic coasts of Europe and North America. Containing a wide range of minerals, vitamins and trace elements, it is used in spa products for its detoxifying and nourishing properties.

Dried carrageen is good for baths and gels as it contains natural polysaccharides which create viscous compounds and it has skin nourishing, softening and protecting qualities. In a bath its softening and protective properties make it ideal for skin irritations and itchiness.

CARRAGEEN BATH RECIPE
Enough for one whole body bath.

15-20g dried Carrageen

Method

See 'Method for dried Seaweed or Carrageen Baths' below.

SEAWEED BATHS

This is an old traditional remedy, which is now popular in spa treatments.

SEAWEED BATH RECIPE
15-20g dried Seaweed

METHOD FOR DRIED SEAWEED OR CARRAGEEN BATHS

1. Soak the dried seaweed or carrageen in lukewarm water for 20 minutes.

2. Then boil the seaweed and soaking water for 15-20 minutes.

3. Add the boiled seaweed and any remaining gel-like seaweed liquid to the bath water.

4. Add further bath water, adjusting the temperature to your liking.

5. Lie in the bath for about 20-30 minutes.

6. Wrap yourself up warmly after your bath and relax quietly for 1 hour.

7. Drink plenty for a day or two after taking a seaweed or carrageen bath.

TIP FOR USING FRESH SEAWEED OR CARRAGEEN

※ You can harvest your own seaweed or carrageen but be careful if there is local pollution. Fresh seaweed or carrageen needs to be used on the same day otherwise it goes dark and rancid. To use it in the bath follow the 'Method for dried Seaweed or Carrageen' above, but skip step 1 of the instructions.

SEAWEED & SALT BATHS

... an excellent detoxifying and rejuvenating spa treatment

Adding salt together with seaweed and placing it in your baths makes an excellent detoxifying and rejuvenating spa treatment for your skin, body and general health and well-being.

SEAWEED AND SALT BATH RECIPES

SEAWEED SALT BATH 1
Stage 1

900g Rough or Dead Sea Salt

Stage 2

100g Dried Seaweed

Method

1. Measure the salt in a bowl.

2. Soak the dried seaweed for 10-15 minutes and then boil it for 20 minutes.

3. Add the salt to the hot, gel-like seaweed liquid before putting it all into the bath water.

4. Use the whole amount in one bath.

5. Lie in the bath for 20-45 minutes and massage your body with the seaweed if you want to. Relax quietly afterwards.

KOMBU SEAWEED SALT BATH
Stage 1

900g Rough or Dead Sea Salt

Stage 2

100g Dried Kombu

Method

1. As carrageen method on the opposite page but leave the kombu to soak for a few hours.

2. Don't use soap or shower gel in the kombu bath.

3. Stay in the bath for 20-45 minutes and relax quietly afterwards.

TIP FOR SEAWEED SALT BATHS

❋ Make sure you put a sieve in the plug hole of your bath otherwise it can get clogged up.

Seaweed Body Wrap

....

INCI names: Lithanium calcareum, Laminaria digitata, Sodium chloride

A good seaweed body wrap cleanses and detoxifies the body and is a classic spa product. The skin absorbs the minerals that are essential for restoring its tone and vitality. These minerals help to disperse local fatty deposits ensuring soft, fresh and healthy looking skin. General application would be for cellulite, connective tissue debility with water retention, slackened dermal tissue after pregnancy and after intensive slimming treatment.

The INCI names above refer to Aromantic's seaweed body wrap, however as a general term, seaweed body wrap refers to a formula, usually powdered, of seaweed, salt and other marine products, which is made into a paste and spread onto the body. This cleanses and detoxifies the body. The skin absorbs the minerals, which are essential for restoring its tone and vitality. The minerals also help to disperse local fatty deposits ensuring soft, fresh and healthy-looking skin.

Instructions for Professional Therapists and Salons

PREPARING THE TREATMENT COUCH

1. Drape the heater blanket on the treatment bench/couch, with one half of the blanket on the couch and one half hanging over the side.

2. Place the cellophane folio wrap on top of the heater blanket, making sure that it hangs down equally on both sides of the couch.

3. Preheat blanket ten minutes before treatment begins.

APPLICATION

1. Mix 250g of the seaweed body wrap powder with approximately 200ml hot water. The substance should be smooth and creamy for easy application.

2. The client should either take off all of their clothes or you can provide them with disposable underwear. While the client is standing up, apply the paste to the entire back of the body with a brush or by hand, starting with the top of the heel, and finishing with the shoulders.

3. Help the client onto the treatment couch and apply the paste to the entire front of the body, starting at the soles of the feet and finishing just below the neck.

4. Wrap the body in the cellophane folio and the heated blanket and allow the client to rest for 30 minutes. The client may experience sweating during this period.

5. Allow the client to wash off the paste under a shower.

6. A period of relaxation of approximately 20 minutes is recommended to support the metabolism-accelerating effect.

7. You can finish with giving your client a light massage using a massage oil or lotion.

TIPS FOR PROFESSIONALS

⚕ Advise the client to drink plenty of water immediately after the treatment and for the next 24 hours.

⚕ For a successful body purge, 5-10 treatments are recommended, minimum twice a week.

INSTRUCTIONS FOR USE AT HOME

WHAT YOU WILL NEED

1. Hot water

2. Seaweed Body Wrap

3. Bin liners or large plastic sheet

4. Clingfilm (the type that's used to cover food)

5. Towels and/or blankets

6. Enough hot water bottles to cover area you've applied paste to

7. Massage Oil or Body Lotion

PREPARING THE SPACE

1. Choose a place in your house where you will be undisturbed for about an hour.

2. Prepare a space where you can lie down comfortably. You may put a camping mattress on the floor, or use your bed but make sure you put down a plastic sheet or several bin liners to lie on. This is to avoid making a mess if you spill some seaweed paste while applying it, removing the clingfilm, or if it leaks out.

3. Warm the room for about 15 minutes before you start.

4. Heat the towels that you will be using to cover yourself.

5. Prepare your hot water bottles in advance.

6. Tear off pieces of clingfilm and place them near where you'll be lying.

7. Have enough water nearby to sip later.

PREPARING YOURSELF AND APPLYING THE SEAWEED BODY WRAP

1. For best results, have a hot bath first, preferably with 5 added tablespoons to half a cup of bath salts, bicarbonate soda or Dead Sea salts. Soak for at least 30 minutes.

2. Keep yourself warm (wrap up in a dressing gown and put on warm socks) while you mix the seaweed body wrap into the hot water (use 250g of the seaweed body wrap powder to approximately 200ml hot water as a guide).

3. Check the heating to make sure that your room will be kept warm for a further full hour.

4. Lie down on your prepared "bed" in your pre-heated room.

5. Apply the seaweed paste to the areas of your body that you would like to treat.

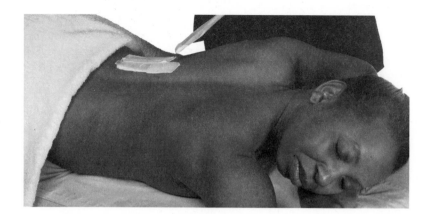

When applying to your back, ask a friend to help…

Tip: If you're going to apply the paste on your back and front, or large areas of the body, you will need a friend to help you.

6. Cover with clingfilm the areas of your body that you have already applied the seaweed paste to.

7. Cover those areas with a pre-warmed towel and then place enough hot water bottles on top of the towel to cover these areas as much as possible.

8. Let the paste do its work by lying as still as you can for about an hour. You may sip some water while you're lying down.

9. You may experience sweating during this period, that's OK.

10. Get up slowly and carefully. If you're dizzy, just keep your head low and wait until it passes.

11. Wash off the paste under a shower.

12. A period of relaxation of approximately 20 minutes is recommended to support the metabolism-accelerating effect.

13. Finish by moisturising your skin with massage oil or a rich, moisturising body lotion.

TIPS FOR HOME USE

✳ Drink plenty of water immediately after and for the next 24 hours.

✳ For a successful body purge, 5-10 treatments are recommended, minimum twice a week.

ACTIVE HEATING MARINE MUD

Active Heating Muds often combine marine mud (sea silt), clay, seaweeds and algae such as spirulina. It is well known that marine mud and algae are rich in positively charged mineral particles and trace elements, mostly because of the high minerality of sea water. According to numerous scientific studies, these natural materials have shown the possibility of ionic exchange capacity through the skin. The detoxification power of active marine muds is also becoming very well known. Sea silt contains a high proportion of minerals and trace elements, which has deep skin cleansing, nourishing, energising, rejuvenating and moisturising properties. It is a dry powder and adding water to it restores its appearance of marine mud, making it possible to apply it as an active heating mud body wrap or face mask as well as to add it to other spa products such exfoliants and scrubs.

Note: Beware that many marine mud products that have water already added contain kathon CG preservative but dried marine products mostly don't have any preservatives added.

HOW TO APPLY ACTIVE HEATING MUD TO THE SKIN - FACE MASKS & BODY WRAPS

1. Mix 50/50 each of the active heating mud and warm water to obtain a smooth uniform paste.

2. Quickly apply in thick layers to areas of the body that need treatment, taking care to previously clean the area to be treated. You might want to use a spatula to apply the mud.

3. If used as a body wrap, wrap the person being treated in warming blankets for 30 minutes or put under an infrared lamp for about 20 minutes.

4. At the end of the treatment, the marine mud should be removed and hot shower taken. To complete the treatment, apply toner followed by moisturiser or body oil to your skin where the marine mud has been used.

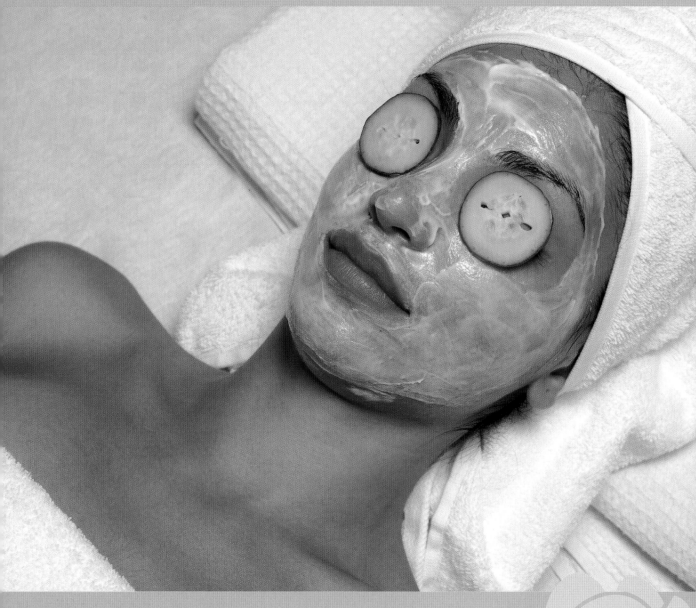

FACE & AROUND THE EYE PRODUCTS

FACE & AROUND THE EYE PRODUCTS

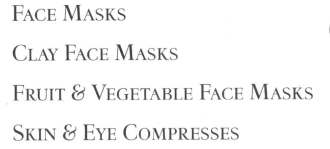

FACE MASKS

CLAY FACE MASKS

FRUIT & VEGETABLE FACE MASKS

SKIN & EYE COMPRESSES

Face and around the eye products such as face masks and compresses are traditionally the most popular symbols of spa treatments. This chapter contains a lot of recipes you can make from what you can find in your kitchen but it also has recipes for making professional products. These facial treatments are usually finished by rinsing your face with warm water, and then applying a skin toner and moisturiser. This will leave your skin refreshed and pampered.

FACE MASKS

. . . .

Face masks and spa treatments seem to be synonymous. Face masks will contain different ingredients depending on the skin type and purpose for which they are used. You may have spots or bad circulation in the skin or your skin type may need moisturising, or a boost of vitamins and minerals. You may have exposed it to too much sun, or stress, or had too little sleep, or you may have been ill or have neglected your skin altogether. Face masks are ideal to use when your skin needs that extra bit of care. A face mask can also be applied to freshen up the skin before going to a party or other special event.

You can make your own face mask using simple ingredients that can be found in your kitchen cupboard. However, you can also easily buy more specialised raw materials, which will enhance the benefits of the masks. Making your own face masks is much less expensive than going to a spa or beauty salon and you will have the satisfaction of using raw materials which are free of preservatives and other artificial ingredients.

RAW MATERIALS FOR FACE MASKS

LIQUIDS

Such as water or other type of liquids with properties suited for different skin types.

DECOCTIONS AND INFUSIONS

Are used in face masks instead of water and for the specific therapeutic benefits and properties of the herbs used.

HYDROLATES

Are commonly used in face masks instead of water for their astringent and other therapeutic properties. Different hydrolates are used for different skin types and conditions.

FRUIT & VEGETABLE JUICES

Lemon juice is very astringent and helps to dissolve the outer layers of the skin. It is therefore very useful in peeling masks. Cucumber juice is astringent and cooling and good for itchy, inflamed or sunburnt skin.

FOOD

Yoghurt, milk, cucumber, avocado, banana.

GELS

Add clays/kaolin to your aloe vera gel or to your own homemade carrageen or flaxseed gel. Sprinkle the clay over the gel while whisking, until it forms a smooth paste. This face mask can be

preserved by adding 1ml/g (20 drops) of preservative to 100ml of face mask.

ESSENTIAL OILS

You can add your own favourite essential oils to your face masks. Caution: use up to a maximum of 10 drops per 100ml of face mask.

VEGETABLE OILS

These help to stop the mask from drying out too quickly.

HONEY

This helps the mask to stick to your face. Face masks with honey cannot be preserved for long.

TIPS FOR MAKING FACE MASKS

* If you have sensitive skin, a small amount of vegetable oil can be added to the recipe, or the face mask can be applied to dry skin which has been covered with a thin layer of oil. Wash the face mask off before it is fully dry. Another alternative is to apply the face mask to clean skin which has been moistened with water.

* If you have normal or oily skin, allow the face mask to dry completely before washing off. Grimacing before washing off the face mask is an effective way of removing dead skin cells. **NB** Moisten the lips before applying the face mask. Apply the face mask onto clean skin. Wash off after 15 minutes with warm water.

* Different types of clay absorb different quantities of liquid so, once you've made your product, you may need to add extra amounts of water and hydrolates (herbal or floral waters) to it to get the consistency right.

* Take your favourite lotion and pour it into a bowl. Then add clay until you get the right consistency of a smooth paste. This is an excellent way to make a moisturising face mask as you will experience a much softer feeling on your face than if you simply used clay and water.

PRESERVING YOUR FACE MASKS

You can add preservatives to lengthen the shelf life of your masks for up to 2 years. Simply add 0.6% preservative, or 1% if you have used gels, infusions or decoctions in your face mask.

NB! You cannot keep face masks containing fresh products such as cucumber, avocado, bananas or honey as they will ferment after a few weeks even with a preservative added.

CLay Face Masks

Clay is rich in minerals and active enzymes, making it beneficial for:

- Stimulating lymph circulation and thereby more efficient waste handling and improvement of cell nutrients.

- Stimulating blood circulation.

- Drawing toxins and superfluous fat and dirt from the skin.

- Contracting and toning the skin.

- Strengthening the connective tissue.

Different coloured clays that I work with come from the different layers in caves in France and are suitable for different skin types and skin conditions:

GREEN CLAY

Oily skin and various skin problems such as acne and eczema

PINK CLAY

For dry and sensitive skin

YELLOW CLAY

For normal and oily skin

RED CLAY

For normal skin

WHITE CLAY OR KAOLIN

For sensitive skin, oily skin and skin with acne

RECIPES FOR CLAY FACE MASKS

BASIC CLAY MASK

For a very simple face mask, mix equal amounts of water and

... clay is rich in minerals and active enzymes ...

clay and add a small quantity of essential oil (1-10 drops per 100ml). *(For how to mix the clay and water successfully, see Method 1-3 on page 67.)*

CLEANSING LAVENDER CLAY MASK

Stage 1

½ tablespoon of Lavender Hydrolate

1 tablespoon Spring Water

1 tablespoon of Clay

Stage 2

1 drop Tea Tree Essential Oil

1 drop Lavender Essential Oil

1 drop Lemon Essential Oil

STIMULATING ROSE CLAY MASK

Stage 1

1 tablespoon of Rose Hydrolate

1 tablespoon of Clay

Stage 2

1ml/g Vitamin E Oil (undiluted)

1ml Evening Primrose Oil

1 drop Sandalwood Essential Oil

1 drop Geranium Essential Oil

Orange Blossom Clay Mask for Sensitive Skin

Stage 1

1 tablespoon of Orange Blossom (Neroli) Hydrolate

1 tablespoon of Clay

Stage 2

2ml of Apricot Kernel Oil

1 drop Mandarin Essential Oil (optional)

Method for Making Clay Face Masks with Hydrolate

1. Place the liquids from stage 1 into a large jug and then simply sprinkle the clay over these liquids.

2. Allow the liquids to absorb the clay for about 10 minutes.

3. Whisk the clay and liquids together.

4. Thoroughly stir stage 2 recipe ingredients into the mixture.

5. Use straight away or finally add a preservative before pouring into jars for keeping. With an added preservative, the face masks will keep for 1.5-2 years.

6. Rinse with warm water, and then use a skin toner and moisturiser cream after. This will leave the skin refreshed and pampered.

Tips for Making Long Shelf-Life Clay Masks

- If your face mask product becomes too dry just add water, especially if it has been stored for more than 1 year.

- If you want to increase the shelf life, add 0.5% undiluted vitamin E oil as an antioxidant in addition to adding 0.6% preservative. See Glossary.

Recipes for Clay Face Masks from Your Kitchen Cupboard

There are many ingredients you can use from your kitchen together with clay to make a variety of face masks for healing purposes. Just remember that the following recipes are for you to make at home and will only last in the fridge for 2-3 days and cannot be preserved and sold as a product.

Banana Clay Face Mask

Stage 1

1 banana (just ripe)

1 tablespoon of honey

1 teaspoon Vegetable Oil (e.g. Olive Oil)

1 tablespoon finely powdered oats

1 tablespoon lemon juice
(squeezed from lemon)

Stage 2

10-15 Essential Oils (optional)

3 tablespoons Clay powder

Method

1. Peel and mash the banana
and add all the other ingredients
except for the clay and essential
oils. You can use your kitchen
liquidiser (ideal) or food blender.
If you don't have these you can
also use an electric stick blender
and a bowl.

2. Pour out the mix from the
blender into a bowl and then
whisk in the clay and eventually
the essential oils. Don't use your
kitchen appliances for clays as
they will make the blades blunt.

3. Apply to your clean face and
neck, leave it on for 10-20 minutes.

4. Rinse with warm water, and
then use a skin toner and moisturiser cream after. This will leave the
skin refreshed and pampered.

AVOCADO CLAY FACE MASK

This face mask is mild, nourishing and vitamin-rich (contains B_5, D, E vita-mins) and is good for people with dry, sensitive, combination, black and ma-ture skin. It has anti-aging properties.

Stage 1

1 Ripe Avocado

2 tablespoons Still Spring Water

Stage 2

2 tablespoons Clay powder

10-15 drops Essential Oils
(optional)

Method

Stage 1: Mash the flesh of the avo-cado with a fork or food processor or electric blender.

Stage 2: Pour the mix from the blender into a bowl and whisk in the clay and eventually the essen-tial oils. Leave the bowl in boiling water for 10-15 minutes so that the contents get warm, then apply this immediately to the skin and leave on for 30 minutes. Rinse off with warm water. You can use cot-ton wool balls if you wish.

AVOCADO/CUCUMBER CLAY FACE MASK

This face mask is good for mature and dehydrated skin as the cucumber has a natural moisturising effect and the avocado is rich in vitamins. I developed this recipe especially for a Ruby Wax television show that I was a guest on.

Stage 1

¼ cup cucumber, peeled and chopped

¼ cup avocado flesh

*There
are many
ingredients
you can
use from
your own
kitchen …*

3 tablespoons finely powdered
oats

2 teaspoons water

1 tablespoon lemon juice
(squeezed from lemon)

1 teaspoon honey

Stage 2

4 tablespoons Clay

10-15 drops of Essential Oils
(optional)

Method

1. Purée the cucumber and avocado flesh in a food processor until it is smooth with the water and lemon juice. Then add all the other ingredients in Stage 1.

2. Pour the mix from the blender into a bowl and then whisk in the clay. Apply to a clean face and neck and leave on for 20-30 minutes. Rinse off with warm water, and then apply a toner and moisturiser.

FRUIT AND CLAY FACE MASK

15ml Apple, pineapple or grapefruit juice

15ml Clay

Method

1. Sprinkle the clay over the juice.

2. Let the clay settle into the juice for 10 minutes.

3. Then whisk the mixture into a fine paste.

4. Apply to clean skin straight away and leave it on for 10-20 minutes.

5. Rinse with warm water, and then use a skin toner and moisturiser cream after. This will leave the skin refreshed and pampered.

Tip

This face mask will not keep so use it all straight away.

Fruit & Vegetable Face Masks From your own Kitchen

....

Recipe Idea: Cucumber and Lemon Face Mask

Benefits of Lemon Juice

Lemon juice is highly astringent and is therefore very effective in reducing wrinkles. It is also good for cleaning wounds (diluted 50% in water to stop bleeding), treating frostbite, insect

Table 5: Fruit and Vegetables to use in Face Masks
For how to prepare the vegetables, see Method For Making Fruit & Vegetable Masks on page 71.

Fruit/Vegetable	Skin Type	Effect on the Skin
Algae	Tired and mature	Refreshes
Apple	Dry, mature	AHA peeling
Papaya	Dry, mature	Peeling effects
Peach	Dry, mature	Soothes
Apricot	Dry, mature, sensitive	Soothes
Avocado	Dry, mature, sensitive	Softens, nourishes, vitamin enrichment
Banana	Dry, mature, sensitive	Softens, refreshes
Cucumber (Juice)	Sensitive	Bleaches, cools
Carrot	Sensitive	Revitalises
Pear	Oily, acne, sensitive	Refreshes, soothes
Potato	Oily, acne, sensitive	Cools
Cabbage, Green	Oily, acne	Draws out in wound compresses
Grapefruit	Oily, acne	Astringent, stimulating
Lemon	Oily, acne	Bleaches, astringent
Pineapple	Oily, acne	Fruit enzymes (bromelain) gently exfoliates skin leaving skin refreshed, soft and clean
Strawberry	Oily, acne	Bleaches
Tomato	Oily, acne	Bleaches
Grapes	All skin types	AHA peeling

bites and general itchiness. Lemon juice helps to dissolve skin and works well in peeling masks and softens hard skin and calluses. If you have calluses, then add 10% carbamide crystals to the recipe. With repeated treatment you can also bleach pigment spots. For skin lightening purposes it is very effective and safe to use.

Recipe

1 lemon providing around 30ml juice (organic is best)

Fine cucumber slices

Method

1. Squeeze the juice from the lemon (heat first to extract more juice).

2. Then dip the cucumber slices into the lemon juice.

3. Apply the cucumber slices to the face.

4. Leave the cucumber on the skin for 15-20 minutes.

5. Don't wash off, simply apply moisturiser over the areas that you applied the face mask to so that it can continue to work without drying out your skin.

Method for Making Fruit and Vegetable Face Masks

1. Grate or purée the fruits and vegetables by hand or by using a food processor.

2. Apply to clean skin for 15-20 minutes.

3. You can also add a little clay to the fruit and vegetable purée. **NB** Take the purée out of your food processor before adding the clay otherwise the clay will blunt the food processor blades.

4. You can also add other raw materials such as finely powdered oats, lemon juice, honey, finely grated almonds, glycerine, and yoghurt to the fruit purées. I believe that organically grown fruit and vegetables are more potent and work better than non-organic.

SKIN & EYE COMPRESSES FROM YOUR OWN KITCHEN

SKIN COMPRESSES

Skin compresses are perfect for spa facials or for other parts of the body that need rejuvenating, rehydrating or soothing. Fruit and vegetable compresses can be soothing, revitalising, cooling and relaxing and can help reduce skin puffiness, dehydration and stress lines.

... soothing, revitalising, cooling and relaxing ...

RECIPES AND METHODS FOR SKIN COMPRESSES

POTATO FACE COMPRESS

Benefits

Cools and reduces swelling and puffiness on the face and the skin around the eyes. Good to use after too much sun.

Ingredients

2-3 organic potatoes (cool in the fridge before use)

Method

1. Peel the potatoes and then finely grate them.

2. Lie down so that the compress will stay on your face.

3. Apply the grated potato to the face, taking care to cover your face, leave on for 30 minutes.

4. Wash off under running water. Apply skin toner and moisturiser.

PAPAYA SKIN COMPRESS

Benefits

The enzyme papain is often known as a biological scalpel.

It dissolves the protein keratin, which holds the dead skin cells on the skin surface, loosening dry skin cells and dead wound tissue without affecting living tissue and fresh skin. Papaya is used in different countries to marinate meat. It can, however, irritate sunburned and infected skin. It also helps to heal certain types of infected wounds by loosening up dead tissue.

Ingredients

4-5 tablespoons of the juice of 1 unripe papaya.

Method

1. Press the peeled fruit with a juicing machine.

2. Soak a cotton cloth with the juice and leave it on the skin for around 30 minutes. The papaya will dissolve the outer layers of the skin.

3. Rinse off with warm water and apply skin toner and moisturiser.

PINEAPPLE SKIN COMPRESS

Benefits

Refreshes the skin and stops inflammation. It is astringent and it dissolves dirt and dead skin cells. Bromelain, the enzyme found in pineapple, has similar properties to papain (see papaya above).

Ingredients

½ fresh pineapple

Method

1. Blend half a peeled pineapple in an electric blender.

2. Spread evenly on the face.

3. Leave on for 15-20 minutes.

4. Rinse off with warm water.

5. Dry with a towel and apply moisturiser to the treated area.

EYE COMPRESSES

The classic symbol of beauty treatment is cucumber slices covering the eyelids. Teabags are often depicted also. Both of these treatments cool and reduce swollen eyes. The Pharoes of Egypt used mother's milk. The skin around the eyes and on the eyelids is very fine and fragile and can't be massaged or exfoliated like the rest of the body butt you can easily make your own eye compresses in your kitchen.

GENERAL METHOD FOR USING LIQUIDS IN EYE COMPRESSES

Including infusions, decoctions, tinctures, fresh juices, and hydrolates.

1. If using any liquids for the compress, soak a very fine piece of cotton cloth or cotton wool in the liquid and squeeze it out lightly so that it is wet. Apply to *closed* eyelids and leave on for 10-15 minutes or you can use freshly brewed herbal, black or green tea teabags and apply them directly onto the closed eyelids if you prefer.

2. When using loose herbs and flowers for infusions and decoctions, it is important to thoroughly strain the strong tea before use.

3. If using sliced fresh vegetables, slice as thinly as possible and place on top of closed eyelids.

4. If using mashed or grated fresh vegetable or botanical material, place the mash on a piece of gauze and then place carefully on closed eyelids.

5. If using hydrolates or tinctures, please dilute (if requested in the recipe) with water according to the instructions in the table below e.g. if it says witch hazel hydrolate (10%) then add 90% water so if the volume of your final product is 100ml, then you would add 10ml hydrolate to 90ml of water.

6. Leave the compress on for up to 15 minutes.

7. Use daily for up to 2 weeks at a time, then give it 2 weeks rest before using the same eye compress recipe again.

Treatments for Various Eye Conditions

Table 6: Puffy and Swollen Eyes

Infusions	Elderflower
	Ribwort leaf (Plantain)
	Chamomile
	Linden Blossom
	Rose petals
Decoctions	Cold strong Black Tea
	Horsetail. It is very important to strain off the silica particles and never use the Horsetail directly on the eyes!
Liquids	Cucumber juice
	Freshly pressed juice of Ribwort leaf (Plantain)
	Rose Hydrolate (100%)
	Witch Hazel Hydrolate (10%)
	Chamomile Hydrolate (10%)
	Arnica Tincture (up to 5%) - use 1 teaspoon of Arnica Tincture to 95ml of cold water *NB Start with lower doses and check your skin's reaction to it.*
Vegetables & Fruits	Finely cut slices of cucumber, raw potatoes or apples. (Use a cheese slicer to cut them as thinly as possible).
	Peel and mash cucumber and place on pieces of gauze over the eyelids.

TABLE 7: DARK RINGS AROUND THE EYES

INFUSIONS	Wormwood
	Peppermint
	Eyebright
OTHER LIQUIDS	Witch Hazel Hydrolate (Up to 20% in cold water)
	Peppermint Hydrolate (Up to 10% in water)
	Skin Lightener with up to 10% Vitamin C
	The juice of 1-2 potatoes
	The juice of 1 apple
	The juice of ½ lemon
VEGETABLES & FRUITS	Finely cut slices of raw potatoes and apples. Finely grate a raw potato or an apple and place on pieces of gauze over closed eyes.

TABLE 8: EYE STYE

INFUSIONS	Chamomile
DECOCTIONS	Fennel
	Horsetail
OTHER LIQUIDS	Chamomile Hydrolate (up to 10% in water)
VEGETABLES	Finely grate a raw potato or an apple and place on pieces of gauze over closed eyes.
OTHERS	Rice flour

TABLE 9: INFLAMED EYELIDS

INFUSIONS	Chamomile (used teabags are good)
	Calendula (Marigold)
	Eyebright
DECOCTIONS	Oak Bark
OTHER LIQUIDS	Aloe Vera Gel
	Flaxseed Gel (*see Glossary*)
OTHER	Fresh Ribwort leaves (Plantain) applied directly on the eyelids. Wash them first in cold water as they can be very dirty and dry them with a towel. Then crush them using a rolling pin or a glass bottle. Once the juice starts to exude from the leaves, place a few of them on each eyelid.

HAND & NAIL
TREATMENTS

HAND & NAIL TREATMENTS

HAND CREAMS

NAIL TREATMENTS

This is a short chapter but has an excellent hand cream recipe to help you look after your often neglected hands, as well as home and professional nail treatments to keep your hands and nails healthy and beautiful.

HAND CREAMS

. . . .

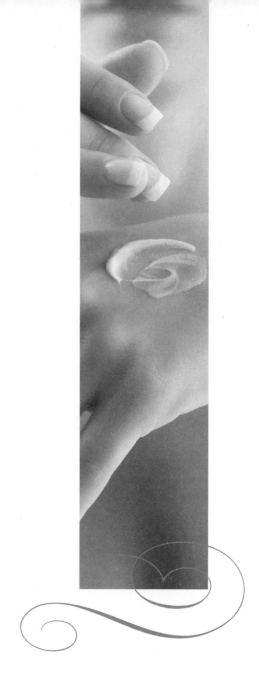

It's common for most of us to have a regular routine for looking after the skin on our face but we don't always think about the rest of our body, particularly our hands.

Caring for your hands is important as they are prone to environmental damage because the skin is fine and the hands have no sebaceous glands. If we have neglected our hands, they can make us look older than our faces do, which is ironic as we spend so much money on making our faces look younger. So, treat your hands the way you would treat your face. The regular use of protective hand cream will help to soften and heal the skin on your hands and to prevent damage that is caused by daily activities and exposure to the elements. Hand creams differ from body creams in that they need to be protective than body creams and provide an important barrier against exposure to water, detergents, pollutants, and the elements. Before applying hand creams,

you can exfoliate the skin on your hands a few times a week, to encourage the growth of new cells. If your hands are very chapped or dry, apply the cream before you go to bed and then put on cotton gloves for an overnight deep moisturising treatment.

Hand Cream Recipe

Rich Hand Cream

This is a rich, emollient and protective barrier hand cream. The jojoba and olive oils and the beeswax or cocoa butter soften, protect and help the skin to hold its moisture by stopping transepidermal water loss (TWL) and helping to keep moisture in the skin. They are also nourishing and softening and provide excellent protection from weather and water. Jojoba oil is considered suitable for all skin types and is a mild and non-irritating oil very protective for the skin. The reason that it is so protective is jojoba is actually a liquid wax, which protects the skin with an invisible film from the

elements. Thistle oil is a good source of the essential fatty acid, Omega 6. Carbamide crystals have softening, moisturising and antiseptic properties. Vitamin E protects the skin from environmental damages and softens the skin.

Fat Stage (75°C-80°C)

  10ml Olive Oil

  10ml Jojoba Oil

  2ml/g Thistle Oil

  1g Beeswax or Cocoa Butter

  2g Cetyl Alcohol

  3g VE Emulsifier

Water Stage (75°C-80°C)

  4.5g MF Emulsifier

  61ml Boiling Spring Water

  12drops/0.6ml/g Preservative

  5g Carbamide Moisturiser Crystals

Third Stage (40°C-35°C)

  1ml/g Vitamin E Oil (undiluted)

Fourth Stage (30-25°C)

  20 drops Essential Oil.

Method

  See page 107.

... treat your hands the way you would treat your face ...

Nail Treatments

A lot of people simply polish their nails but don't really care for them. I have included a few simple treatments that are inexpensive, easy to make at home and won't take much effort to incorporate into your personal care routine. High street nail products usually contain many harmful chemicals. With these nail treatments you'll be using safe, natural ingredients.

Nail Treatment Recipes

PROFESSIONAL/COMMERCIAL PRODUCTS

Nail Nourisher for Brittle Nails

58ml Sesame Oil

20ml Peach Kernel Oil

10ml Borage Oil

10ml Vitamin E Oil (undiluted)

2% Essential Oils (10 drops each each of Myrrh, Tea Tree, Rosemary, Lemon and Lavender)

Cuticle Oil

This oil dries quickly and nourishes the cuticles.

5ml Jojoba Oil

30ml Sesame Oil

12ml Peach Kernel Oil

10ml Apricot Kernel Oil

30ml Borage Oil

10ml Vitamin E Oil (undiluted)

1ml/g Vitamin A Palmitate

25 drops Myrrh Essential Oil

25 drops Lemon Essential Oil

METHOD FOR NAIL NOURISHER AND CUTICLE OIL

1. Measure the ingredients and mix them together in a beaker or jug.

2. Pour into bottles.

3. **Note**: If you want to sell these products, then we strongly recommend that you add 5 drops of rosemary CO_2 extract in order to protect the large amounts of vitamin E in the blends. If you do this, the products will keep for up to 2 years, instead of 7-8 months.

Orange Blossom Hydrolate Treatment (for bleaching nails)

90ml Orange Blossom Hydrolate

8ml Glycerine

2g Citric Acid

Method

1. Measure and blend everything together.

2. Brush onto your nails or dip your nails into the solution.

This product keeps for 1.5-2 years.

NAIL TREATMENTS FROM YOUR KITCHEN

COMPRESS FOR CUTICLE INFECTION

9g Honey

1ml/g Horseradish, finely grated

Method

1. Blend the (9g) of honey with 10% (1ml/g) of finely grated horseradish root.

2. Apply the mixture to cuticles and then cover with cotton gloves and finally with plastic gloves (or a plastic bag).

3. Leave on overnight.

4. Remove plastic and cotton gloves and wash off the mixture with warm water.

LEMON TREATMENT (FOR BLEACHING NAILS)

1 lemon (preferably organic)

Method

1. Cut a lemon in half and dig your nails into the lemon, moving the fingertips back and forth.

2. The juice will destroy the dead tissue around the nails and the cuticles. This treatment is quite strong and should not be used too often.

LEMON AND MYRRH NAIL TREATMENT

Myrrh helps to heal wounds; it is an astringent and gives shine to the nails. It also has bleaching and strengthening properties if used daily.

30ml Lemon juice (1 lemon)

5ml Glycerine

5ml Myrhh Tincture

Method

1. Squeeze the juice from the lemon.

2. Add the other ingredients.

3. Apply to your nails with a brush or dip your nails into the solution.

4. Keep in the fridge and use within 14 days.

TREATMENT FOR BRITTLE NAILS

Internally: Take Silica, Vitamin A, B and D, and Zinc tablets.

Skin Exfoliants, Peelers, Cleansers & Toners

Skin Exfoliants, Peelers, Cleansers & Toners

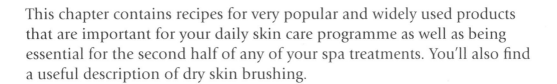

Skin Exfoliants

Skin Peelers

Skin Cleansers

Skin Toners

This chapter contains recipes for very popular and widely used products that are important for your daily skin care programme as well as being essential for the second half of any of your spa treatments. You'll also find a useful description of dry skin brushing.

SKIN EXFOLIANTS

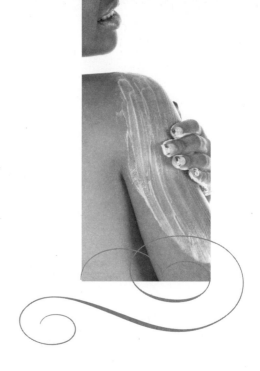

Exfoliation is a cosmetic technique for removing dead skin and stimulating the growth of soft, new skin. It exposes the healthy, supple, smooth skin underneath the dead skin cells, giving the skin a fresh and rejuvenated appearance. Many skin problems are associated with an excessive build up of dead skin cells, which can make the skin thick and lacklustre by clogging the pores. Skin aging, sun damage, acne and hyper-pigmentation can all also be helped by regular skin exfoliation. Our skin does exfoliate itself, but this naturally occurring process can slow down as we age. Skin exfoliation is a commonly skipped step in the usual beauty regime of cleansing, toning and moisturising. The other advantage is that after an exfoliating treatment, the pores can be much more thoroughly cleansed and the skin is more receptive to any skin care products that you apply.

Mechanical exfoliants include salt and sugar body scrubs and polishes, micro-bead or grain scrubs e.g. jojoba exfoliating grains, crushed nut shells, pumice, a brush and abrasive cloths such as synthetic exfoliating and abrasive gloves, a loofah or the technique of dry skin brushing. Please be aware that the definitions of exfoliation and peeling *(see page 88)* differ in different countries and I have chosen to use the definitions most widely accepted in the United Kingdom.

In this book I have included recipes for a body scrub and polish that consist of vegetable oils (types that are not too fatty such as thistle, jojoba, sesame seed or avocado) and an abrasive ingredient along with other raw materials

such as essential oils. In commercial products, sea salt is mainly used as the abrasive ingredient in body polishes, scrubs or other exfoliant products but a newer development is the use of brown sugar. If using salt, you can choose from kitchen salt, fine grained sea salt or fine-grained Dead Sea salt. It is best if the granules are round and soft and not sharp like rough sea salt, which can tear and damage the skin.

DRY SKIN BRUSHING

An excellent way to exfoliate the skin

Before we get to the recipes for skin exfoliants, let's have a look at dry skin brushing, variations of which have been practised for thousands of years. Dry skin brushing is a simple, inexpensive way to support your immune system and to stimulate your lymphatic system to clean itself of toxins and accumulated acids, which in turn, accelerates and enhances the body's natural detoxification processes. This simple technique is great for skin exfoliation, which also helps the skin to eliminate toxins by keeping the pores open. And even better it helps your skin to rejuvenate and to regain a soft, youthful glow and also helps to reduce cellulite by decongesting veins and the lymphatic system.

Done properly, dry skin brushing benefits mature skin by stimulating both the sweat and oil glands, contributing to the restoration of moist, supple skin and strengthening the skin pores.

It is important that you use a natural and not synthetic bristle brush as a synthetic brush will scratch the surface of your skin. Buy either a long-handled, or rounded, brush with bristles that are neither too stiff nor too soft. It shouldn't scratch, but you should feel some friction against the skin. These should be available from most health food and department stores.

To achieve the skin stimulating effect, don't wet your skin before you start brushing, and make sure that your brush is dry. This is very important as any exposure to water will soften the brush's bristles, depriving it of it's stimulating effect.

The entire surface of the skin should be brushed, with the exception of any broken or cracked skin, etc, and the face, which is too sensitive to be brushed. Immediately before showering or bathing, start with the feet and gently brush up toward the heart. This is very important, you must always brush towards the heart. Brush gently in a circular motion around your abdomen (counter-clockwise) and breasts/chest area. It only takes a minute or two and you can repeat the process if you wish.

For optimal results, dry skin brushing is best done at least once, if not twice, on a daily basis. It is highly recommended you start your spa experience with a few minutes of dry skin brushing and follow it up with a hydrotherapy treatment such as an alkaline or Kneipp bath, or even just a shower.

Dry skin brushing can become a highly addictive, but healthy, activity!

Dry brushing is a simple technique that is great for skin exfoliation…

RECIPES AND METHODS FOR SKIN EXFOLIANTS

SEA SALT BODY SCRUB

This exfoliating salt scrub is a wonderful blend of skin-polishing sea salt in moisturising vegetable oils that will resurface the skin, leaving it super smooth and rejuvenated.

100g Fine Dead Sea Salt/Sea Salt

3-6 drops non-water based Colour

30-40ml Vegetable Oil

1ml/g Vitamin E Oil (undiluted)

20-40 drops Essential Oils

SUGAR BODY POLISH

This body polish is a luxurious blend of sugar in vitamin-rich and cleansing oils that is suitable for dry/sensitive skin. If you do have sensitive skin, remember to add essential oils that are suitable, such as lavender, chamomile, etc.

100g Brown Sugar

5ml Thistle Oil

5ml Avocado Oil

5ml Castor Oil

2ml/g Vitamin E Oil (undiluted)

20-25 drops Essential Oils

METHOD FOR MAKING BODY POLISHES AND SCRUBS

1. Mix all of the ingredients together and fill into jar and label.

2. These products will keep for 1 year.

METHOD FOR USING BODY POLISH AND SCRUBS

1. When you are showering, take a portion of your body polish into your hand and gently "polish" your body using a firm but gentle circular motion, paying particular attention to the dry areas of your skin.

2. Wash off the body polish while you're showering.

3. Remember to take extra care as the oils in your body polish can make the shower floor or bath quite slippery.

4. Scrubs and polishes will exfoliate dead skin cells and moisturise your body, but you may need to apply another moisturiser once you've dried your skin, depending on how your skin feels.

... leave your skin super smooth and rejuvenated ...

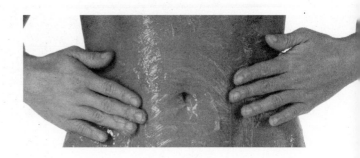

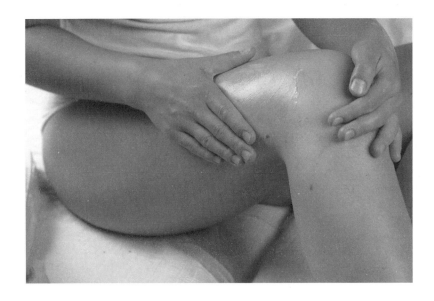

... after exfoliating, the skin is more receptive to any skin care products that you apply ...

FACE AND BODY EXFOLIATING CREAM FOR DRY/MATURE/ SENSITIVE SKIN

An exfoliating cream is abrasive and removes dead skin cells. The base in this case consists of a cream made with castor and other vegetable oils with the addition of vegetable-based peeling grains such as jojoba. This recipe makes 100ml of exfoliating cream. This exfoliating cream is suitable for use on the face.

Fat Stage (75-80°C)

8ml Castor Oil

4ml Macadamia Nut Oil

4ml Apricot Kernel Oil

2gr Shea Butter

2gr Cetyl Alcohol

3gr VE Emulsifier

Water Stage (75-80°C)

5gr MF Emulsifier

67ml Rose Hydrolate *or* Boiling Water

3ml/g Glycerine

0.6ml/g (12 drops) Preservative

Third Stage (40-35°C)

2ml/g Vitamin E Oil (undiluted)

Fourth Stage (30-25°C)

10 drops Geranium Essential Oil

5 drops Petitgrain Essential Oil

5 drops Lavender Essential Oil

Fifth Stage (25°C)

2-5g Jojoba Exfoliating Grains

Method

See Method for making Exfoliating, Peeling and Cleansing Creams on page 90.

Skin Peelers

. . . .

Again, please be aware that the definitions of exfoliation (see page 84) and peeling differ in different countries and I have chosen to use the definitions most widely accepted in the United Kingdom. So, when I use the words 'peeling agent', 'skin peeler', 'peeling' or 'peeler' I am referring to chemical skin peelers. However, I advocate the use of natural chemical peeling agents such as detergents, salicylic acid, glycolic acid, alpha hydroxy acids (AHAs) or beta hydroxy acids (BHAs), fruit enzymes, citric acid, lactic or malic acids in varying concentrations.

Chemical skin peeling is a method of peeling the outer layers of the skin by creating, what is in effect a chemical burn. As the burn heals, skin regeneration takes place and a new layer of skin is formed, which is pinker, smoother and tauter. There are different degrees of chemical skin peeling, ranging from very superficial peeling to deep peeling. The depth of the chemical burn is dependent on a number of factors, such as the chemical mixture and concentration used, the length of time of the chemical's contact with the skin and whether or not the therapist places an occlusive dressing over the area being peeled. The levels of pain experienced depend on the depth of peeling. Superficial peeling doesn't involve any pain. The recipe below makes use of betaine detergent for its mild and gentle skin peeling qualities, which offers superficial skin peeling.

Recipe for Skin Peeler

Mild Peeling Cream with Soap for All Skin Types, Except Sensitive Skin

A peeling cream that can be used for a very superficial skin peel and used for thoroughly removing surface impurities from the skin while being soothing and softening to the skin. It is gentle enough to be used in the morning and evening. This cream is suitable for use on the face.

Fat Stage (75-80°C)

9ml Castor Oil

8ml Jojoba Oil

2gr Cetyl Alcohol

1g Cocoa Butter

3g VE Emulsifier

Water Stage (75-80°C)

5gr MF Emulsifier

54ml Boiling Water

5ml/g Glycerine

0.6ml/g (12 drops) Preservative

Third Stage (40-35°C)

10ml Beta Detergent

1ml/g Vitamin E Oil (undiluted)

Fourth Stage (25°C)

10 drops Ylang Ylang Essential Oil

5 drops Geranium Essential Oil

5 drops Lemon Essential Oil

Skin Cleansers

A cleanser is a facial care product that is used to remove skin surface impurities, traces of make-up, dead skin cells, excessive oiliness, dirt and other types of pollutants from the skin of the face and helps the skin to breathe. Cleansing the skin helps to unclog pores and prevent skin conditions such as acne and is necessary for all skin types.

Cleansing with a good quality cleanser is an essential step before toning and moisturising the skin and most people include this in their daily beauty regimes. Cleansing is different from exfoliating in that exfoliating isn't always performed every day whereas cleansing is often done twice a day, in the morning and at night. Some, however, do like to cleanse their skin after they have exfoliated it. Others think that this is too much. It all depends on individual taste and skin condition.

Recipes for Cleansing Creams

In these recipes the cleansing base is in the form of cream. Castor oil, which is an excellent oil for cleansing, is used because it does not get absorbed so quickly by the skin. Instead, castor oil draws the dirt out to itself. The cleansing cream needs to be washed off with water as it contains a detergent.

Cleansing Cream for All Skin Types

It is gentle enough to be used in the morning and evening. This cream is suitable for use on the face.

Fat Stage (75-80°C)

12ml/g Castor Oil

2g Shea Butter

8ml Apricot Kernel Oil

2g Cetyl Alcohol

1g Cocoa Butter

3g VE Emulsifier

Water Stage (75-80°C)

5g MF Emulsifier

54ml Boiling Water

3ml/g Glycerine

0.6ml/g (12 drops) Preservative

Third Stage (40-35°C)

1ml/g Vitamin E Oil (undiluted)

Fourth Stage (25°C)

10-15 drops Essential Oil

Cleansing is often done twice a day, in the morning and at night…

METHOD FOR MAKING EXFOLIATING, PEELING AND CLEANSING CREAMS

1. **Fat Stage:** Heat the fat stage ingredients in a double boiler until all of the ingredients have melted and the temperature has risen to 75-80°C. There is no need to use a whisk at this stage.

2. **Water Stage:** After boiling the spring water in a kettle, measure it according to the recipe and pour it over the rest of the water stage ingredients, which you have put into a separate double boiler.

3. Whisk the water stage ingredients well together, making sure that the MF emulsifier powder is fully dissolved in the water and that you don't have any lumps. Then allow the mixture to heat to 75-80°C.

4. When both fat and water stages are over 75°C, remove both double boilers from the hob, keeping the water stage mixture hot by leaving it on the top half of the double boiler.

5. Now pour the melted **fat stage into the water stage** in a thin, steady stream, while continuously whisking the mixture from side to side for 5 minutes.

6. Allow the mixture to cool, stirring all the time. You can speed up by the cooling process by replacing the hot water in the double boiler with very COLD water. In the process of cooling down, the mixture becomes a cream and will reach its thickest consistency when it is has cooled down to room temperature.

7. **Third Stage:** stir in the third stage ingredients when the mixture has cooled to under 40°C.

8. **Fourth Stage:** Continue stirring until the mixture has cooled to under 30°C, then thoroughly mix in the essential oils.

9. **Fifth Stage for the exfoliating cream:** stir in the exfoliating grains with a spoon or spatula (don't whisk).

10. Pour the cream into one big jar or smaller jars and label.

Skin Toners

. . . .

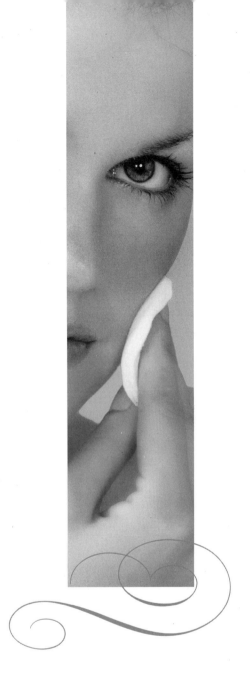

Skin toners are an essential part of any spa treatment. After the skin has been cleansed, skin toners are applied for their astringent qualities, cleaning and reducing the size of the pores and wrinkles so that dust and dirt will not enter as easily - avoiding further skin problems. Toners can also be used to disinfect and freshen up the skin, leaving a trace of essential oil. They are easily applied with cotton wool or can be sprayed on and then wiped off with cotton wool.

The 'water' part of skin toners can consist of: spring water; hydrosols; or herbal infusions, decoctions or tinctures and further personalised by adding different water-soluble ingredients mentioned in the recipes below.

Recipes for Skin Toners

Rejuvenating

76ml Rose Hydrolate

10ml Orange Blossom Hydrolate

5ml Frankincense Hydrolate

5ml Peppermint Hydrolate

2ml/g Sea Silk

2ml NFF Moisturiser

After Sun Soothing Spray

79ml Still Water

10ml Aloe Vera Concentrate

5ml Lavender Hydrolate

3ml/g Comfrey Glycerol Extract

2ml/g D-Panthenol

1ml/g (20 drops) Preservative

Oily/Acne Skin

80ml Geranium Hydrolate

5ml Chamomile Hydrolate

5ml Lavender Hydrolate

3ml/g Comfrey Glycerol Extract

5ml Aloe Vera Concentrate

2ml/g AHA Natural Fruit Acids

DRY/MATURE SKIN
75ml Rose Hydrolate

10ml Orange Blossom Hydrolate

5ml Witch Hazel Glycerol Extract

5ml Ginseng Tincture

5ml Calendula Tincture

SENSITIVE SKIN 1
80ml Orange Blossom Hydrolate

14ml Rose Hydrolate

3m/g Comfrey Glycerol Extract

3ml Aloe Vera Concentrate

SENSITIVE SKIN 2
90ml Rose Hydrolate

3ml/g Comfrey Glycerol Extract

5ml Aloe Vera Concentrate

2ml/g D-Panthenol

CONCENTRATION & UPLIFTING SPRAY
60ml Rosemary Hydrolate

20ml Geranium Hydrolate

15ml Peppermint Hydrolate

5ml Frankincense Hydrolate

GENERAL METHOD FOR MAKING SKIN TONERS

1. Measure the ingredients ina meas-uring beaker or cylinder, adding one on top of each other until you reach the 100ml.

2. Pour the mixture into a bottle and shake it.

3. Use a spray cap or spray bottle for the best results.

TIPS FOR MAKING AND USING SKIN TONERS

* I recommend that you shake the bottle before each use.

* All facial waters which contain acidic ingredients like aloe vera and lactic acid tend to separate when mixed with herbal infusion. This is normal and does not affect the product in any way. Simply shake the bottle before use.

* The shelf life of the toners in this book without added preservatives is 6-8 months. If preservatives are added, the shelf life is increased to 2 years; simply add 10 drops of preservative per 100ml recipe.

Skin Moisturising & Nourishing Treatments

Skin Moisturising & Nourishing Treatments

Skin & Massage Products

Massage Bars

Skin Rejuvenation & Anti-Wrinkle Products

Body Butters

Creams

In this chapter you will find recipes to give you some ideas for moisturising, softening, protecting and nourishing the skin after your spa treatments or for daily use. Moisturising and nourishing the skin after a spa treatment is very important and this stage should not be left out. Moisturising your skin after cleansing and toning is also important and these recipes can be used for your daily skin care programme.

I've included a lot of different types of recipes so that you have a lot to choose from when it comes to caring for your skin after a spa treatment.

Skin & Massage Products

. . . .

Skin and Body Massage Oils

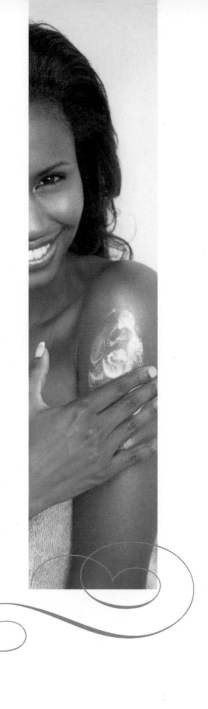

It is very simple to make a massage oil blend for yourself, friends and family or for your customers and clients. These recipes are tailor-made to different skin types and conditions. They are well proven and will offer excellent lubricating, but also nourishing, properties, both of which are important for a massage oil. If you wish, you can add 12-15 drops of essential oils of your choice to the formulas in these tables. To make, simply measure and mix the oils together, bottle and store in an airtight container in a cool place away from direct sunlight.

Note: When adding more than 2% undiluted vitamin E oil to any blend, I recommend that you also add from 5-10 drops of rosemary botanical CO_2 extract to protect the vitamin E oil from going rancid, as the extract is a more stable anti-oxidant than vitamin E oil. If you do this, the shelf life will be 1.5-2 years.

... recipes with excellent lubricating and nourishing properties ...

TABLE 10: PERCENTAGES OF BODY MASSAGE OILS TO BLEND TO MAKE 100%

	Dry Skin	Black Skin (Dry)	Mature Skin	Black Skin (Mature)	Sensitive Skin	Black Skin (Sensitive)	Oily Skin	Rheumatism	Itchy Skin	Sun Protection
Macadamia Nut	40		20	30	30	30				
Apricot Kernel		15	20		50	40				
Peach Kernel				10	10	10	30			
Rice Bran		30	10						20	10
Rosehip					5	10	18	25	15	20
Castor	5		5			5		10		
Borage			10		5		10			10
Evening Primrose		10	10	10			10	5	10	
Vitamin E (undiluted)	10	2	5	2	5	2	3	5	20	40
Coconut Butter (melted)		15			15	10				
Jojoba		15	10		10		18	15		
Avocado		23	50		40		40			
Grape Seed				13		20	20	20	35	
Thistle	45		5	33	25	7	27	32	50	20
Essential Oils (drops)	12-15	12-15	12-15	12-15	12-15	12-15	12-15	12-15	12-15	12-15
%	100	100	100	100	100	100	100	100	100	100

Massage Bars

. . . .

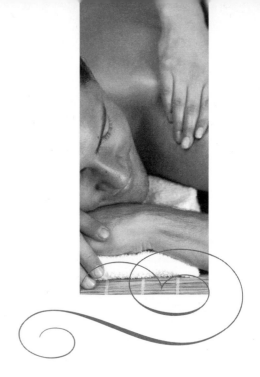

Massage oil is not always easy to use. Massage bars melt easily in your hands so you can use just the right amount every time and they're perfect for all skin types and conditions except for oily skin or facial large pores. They make great gifts for friends and family and they're ideal to use in the sauna.

How to Use Your Massage Bars

Take the massage bar in your hands, squeeze it with a firm pressure and rub it between your hands. As it starts to melt, apply the bar to the skin in a circular motion. You then put the bar aside and massage normally, applying the bar again only when you need more lubrication. The massage bar will stop melting when you put it aside and away from a heat source like the skin.

Massage Bar Recipes

Vitamin Massage Bar

Stage 1

80g Cocoa Butter

10g Shea Butter

5g Hemp Seed Oil

5 drops Carotene

Stage 2

2ml/g Vitamin E Oil (undiluted)

1ml/g Vitamin A Palmitate

2ml/g (50 drops)Essential Oils

GLA Massage Bar

Stage 1

80g Cocoa Butter

8g Beeswax

3g Shea Butter

Stage 2

5ml Borage Oil

2ml/g Vitamin E Oil (undiluted)

2ml/g (50 drops)Essential Oils

General Method for Making Massage Bars

1. **Stage 1:** Place all of the Stage 1 ingredients in a saucepan and melt slowly under steady supervision so that it does not burn.

2. Cool down by placing the saucepan in a bigger saucepan containing very cold water until the mixture thickens around the edges. Stir occasionally as it cools. Do not allow to thicken too much, you should still be able to pour the mixture.

3. **Stage 2**: Add the pre-measured stage 2 ingredients such as essential oils and stir well. Do not allow the mixture to thicken too much - you should still be able to pour it.

4. Pour the mixture quickly into the mould tray. The easiest moulds to work with are silicone moulds.

5. Put the tray in a fridge until the massage bars are hard or leave outside the fridge overnight to harden.

6. Once hardened, simply turn the mould upside down and press with your fingers on the back of the mould so that the bars fall out. If they don't fall out by themselves, knock the mould tray against the table and they'll usually fall out. You can also put the mould tray in the freezer for ½ to1 hour before knocking removing the bars from the tray.

TIPS FOR MAKING MASSAGE BARS

⁂ Adding 8-15% beeswax to your massage bar will allow it to melt slower and last longer. Beeswax holds the bar together and makes them harder so its easier to get them out of the moulds. The beeswax bars also give more protection to the skin. When adding beeswax, reduce cocoa butter accordingly. **NB** Do not use beeswax for people with oily or large-pored skin because the wax will clog their pores.

⁂ A good way to store your massage bars is in a box with greaseproof paper between the layers of bars.

⁂ If your bars are too soft, crack or don't fall out of the moulds, simply re-melt them, adding a little more essential oils and pour when like soup.

⁂ Use simple moulds without too much detail. Round moulds are easier to use than square ones.

⁂ You can buy muffin moulds to make larger massage bars (50-70g).

⁂ Don't use moulds with too wide a diameter as they crack more easily.

⁂ If the mixture has cooled down too much before you tried to pour it into the mould tray it may develop a thick porridge-like consistency, which makes it impossible to pour. Simply reheat the mixture, cool it down again and pour when the consistency is similar to a soup.

Skin Rejuvenation & Anti-Wrinkle Products

These anti-aging oil blends and serums are very easy to blend apply to the fine skin around the eyes and eyelids. They are based on high dosages of vitamins for antioxidant and anti-aging purposes. We also use vegetable oils with high quantities of omega 3 fatty acid, which will nourish the skin.

Face Oils & Anti-Wrinkle Oils

These recipes for face and anti-wrinkle oils are tailor-made to different skin types and conditions. They are simple to make but vitamin-rich and effective. As a general rule, apply twice a day for a skin rejuvenating boost. These oils are very dry, thin, soft and smooth. If you wish, you can add 12-15 drops of essential oils of your choice to the formulas in these tables. To make, simply measure and mix the oils together, bottle and store in an airtight container in a cool place away from direct sunlight.

Note: When adding more than 5% undiluted vitamin E oil to any blend, I recommend that you also add 5-10 drops of rosemary botanical CO_2 extract per 100ml of blend to protect the vitamin E oil from going rancid, as the extract is a more stable antioxidant than vitamin E oil. If you do this, the shelf life will be 1.5-2 years.

Anti-Aging Eye Oil Recipes

Please note: These recipes will not treat eye diseases or eyesight problems. They are for nourishing the skin around the eyes.

Anti-Aging Eye Oil for very sensitive and oily skin
90ml Rosehip Oil

10ml Vitamin E Oil (undiluted)

Anti-Aging Eye Oil for mature and dry skin
75ml Rosehip Oil

10ml Macadamia Nut Oil

15ml Vitamin E Oil (undiluted)

Eye Oil for infections
This Anti-Aging Eye Oil is also good for treating skin infections around the eyes.

65ml Rosehip Oil

20ml Borage Oil

13ml Vitamin E Oil (undiluted)

2ml/g Vitamin A Palmitate

TABLE 11: PERCENTAGES OF FACE & ANTI-WRINKLE OILS TO BLEND TO MAKE 100%.

	Dry Skin	Black Skin (Dry)	Mature Skin		Black Skin (Mature)	Sensitive Skin		Black Skin (Sensitive)		Oily Skin		Scar Tissue		Acne Oil	
Borage						10				20			20	10	20
Evening Primrose		10		10	20				5	20	5	7				
Rosehip				15		20		30		60	50	25	15	35	50
Apricot Kernel	10			20			50		20							
Peach Kernel		20	15											15	10
Camelina	10	10					20		20		35		15		
Macadamia Nut			30		30	10									
Thistle	15	10	40		20				20	10		25		15	
Vitamin E	15	20	15	10	15	10	20	15	15	5	8	50	50	15	10
Sweet Almond	50														
Avocado		30		50		60		50	5						
Shea Butter Oil					10										
Jojoba														10	10
Essential Oils (drops)	12-15	12-15	12-15	12-15	12-15	12-15	12-15	12-15	12-15	12-15	12-15	12-15	12-15	12-15	12-15
%	100	100	100	100	100	100	100	100	100	100	100	100	100	100	100

Note: For an extra boost, you can add these anti-aging ingredients at the following dosages to your chosen and remember to reduce the amount of one of the vegetable oils in your blend accordingly. Hyaluronic Acid - use 1%; Remodelling Intense – use up to 2%; Q10 Plus E – use up to 0.5-2% or for intensive treatment use 4%.

(NB: Be very careful when applying essential oils on the face or around the eyes. The skin around the eyes, in particular, is very sensitive).

Rejuvenate the eye area with vitamin-rich, anti-aging eye oils…

Anti-Aging Eye Blend

This Blend is also good for reducing puffiness around the eyes.

75ml Rosehip Oil

15ml Vitamin E Oil (undiluted)

5ml Borage Oil

3ml Arnica Tincture

2ml Eyebright Tincture

Method for Making Eye Oils and Blends

1. Simply blend the ingredients in a bottle and shake well before use.

2. Apply directly around the eyes in the evenings or whenever your eyes need extra attention.

Note: If you want to sell these oil blends, then we strongly recommend that you add 5-8 drops of rosemary CO_2 extract in order to protect the large amounts of vitamin E in the blends. If you do this, the products will keep for up to 2 years, instead of 7-8 months.

Anti-Aging Skin Serums

You can help reduce the signs of aging in the face and around the eyes by using super potent active raw materials in a mainly oil-based blend called a 'serum'. Serums prevent premature signs of aging as they contain high doses of antioxidants, which work on the skin if used regularly and thereby reducing damage caused by the aging of the connective tissue such as elastin and collagen.

An oil serum will feel dry on the skin as it is usually absorbed quickly by the skin. This is because oil serums should contain thin, dry oils rich in omega 3 & 6 essential fatty acids combined with antioxidants such as vitamins E and A as well as rosemary CO_2 extract. And so important oils for making serums are kiwi seed, camelina, chia seed, rosehip seed, hemp seed, evening primrose, borage and thistle. Serums are used on specific parts of your skin, usually the face and around the eyes to effect an intensive cure.

A serum is best applied in the evenings after you have cleansed your face and applied a toner.

TABLE 12: RECIPES FOR EXTRA INTENSIVE FACE & AROUND THE EYE
SERUMS

	Dry Skin 1	Dry Skin 2	Mature Skin 1	Mature Skin 2	Sensitive Skin 1	Sensitive Skin 2	Oily Skin
Vitamin E (undiluted)	30	34	30	33	30	35	10
Camelina Oil	25	30	42	10	10		33
Hemp Seed Oil	30	25	10	20	10	20	30
Rosehip Oil	4			10	45	28	
Macadamia Nut Oil		2	10	7			
Kiwi Seed Oil	8	5	3	16		12	21
Vitamin A Palmitate	1	1	1	1	2	1	2
Sea Buckthorn CO_2 Extract	1		1			1	1
Remodelling Intense		2	2	2	2	2	2
Rosemary Antioxidant (drops)	8-10	8-10	8-10	8-10	8-10	8-10	8-10
Essential Oils (drops)	8-12	8-12	8-12	8-12	8-12	8-12	8-12
%	100	100	100	100	100	100	100

NB: Be very careful when applying essential oils on the face or around the
eyes. The skin around the eyes, in particular, is very sensitive.

BODY BUTTERS

. . . .

I have especially developed these body butter recipes for you to make them without any heating. With this simple method it's very easy to just mix together. There are some harder butters such as cocoa and mango that have high melting points that are impossible to work with using this technique. They would have to be heated and that is a different procedure altogether.

These butters will help treat dry patches on the hands, feet, elbows and any other dry patches that you may have. The butters are not suitable for use on the face for oily or large-pored skin types.

BODY BUTTER 1

This Body Butter is nourishing and soothing, which helps cell rejuvenation and helps protect the skin from the sun.

Stage 1

40g Coconut Butter

35g Avocado Butter

20g Shea Butter

Stage 2

2ml/g Vitamin E Oil (undiluted)

1ml/g Vitamin A Palmitate

1ml/g Sea Buckthorn CO_2 Extract

Stage 3

20-25 drops (1ml) Essential Oils OR 20-25 drops (1ml) Organic Aroma

BODY BUTTER 2

This Body Butter is excellent for skin rejuvenation as well as for black skin.

Stage 1

55g Avocado Butter

20g Coconut Butter

20g Shea Butter

Stage 2

2ml/g Vitamin E Oil (undiluted)

2ml/g Remodelling Intense

5-6 drops Carotene (optional – it will make your butter an orange colour)

Stage 3

20-25 drops (1ml) Essential Oils OR 20-25 drops (1ml) Organic Aroma

Body Butter 3

This Body Butter is excellent for skin rejuvenation. **Note:** *you could replace the sunflower oil with other vegetable oils of your own choice; I would recommend oils high in omega 6 and 3 essential fatty acids, such as kiwi seed, camelina, rosehip, thistle or chia seed.*

Stage 1

73g Coconut Butter (aroma retained)

15g Shea Butter

5ml/g Sunflower Oil

Stage 2

2ml/g Vitamin E Oil (undiluted)

1ml/g Vitamin A Palmitate

2ml/g Remodelling Intense

Stage 3

20-25 drops (1.6ml/g) Organic Coconut Aroma

Method for Making the Body Butters

1. Measure the stage 1 ingredients and place in a plastic or stainless steel bowl.
2. Use a handheld electric blender (also called a stick blender) and work on the butters so that they start mixing together. Use a plastic or wooden spatula to remove the butter that gets stuck to the blades of the blender.
3. When the butters start 'moussing' together like a smooth whipped cream consistency, you can then switch to a hand whisk, making sure to whip the mixture up as much as possible. First make sure that there are no lumps as the lumps are difficult to get rid of with a hand whisk.
4. Whisk in stage 2 ingredients, making sure that they are thoroughly mixed in.
5. Whisk in stage 3 ingredients, making sure that they are evenly distributed in the mixture. Adjust the fragrance if necessary.
6. Spoon into jars and label.

Tips for Making Your Body Butters

- Once you've mastered the technique, its easier to multiply the recipe to, for example, 400-500g as it will be easier to blend with the electric blender. I suggest you at least double these recipes to total 200g as 100g is a bit difficult to manage with an electric blender.
- Adding organic aromas *(see Glossary)* will give your butter a wonderful fragrance. Use 1-1.5% instead of essential oils.
- Adding colour improves their appeal. Always use non-water based colours or natural ingredients such as carotene or sea buckthorn CO_2 extract.
- Be aware that the consistency of these butters will take a day or two after making it to firm up.
- Keep your butter in a cool environment otherwise it will liquify. It will firm up again though when its placed in a cool or cold environment for a while. This is normal for butters made in this way.

CREAMS

Making your own creams and moisturisers is simple, easy and interesting. There are a few simple rules that must be followed but, beyond these, there are endless possibilities for inventing and making your own unique creams for different purposes *and* you'll know exactly what the creams contain. If there is an ingredient you're allergic to you can often leave it out or replace it with something else.

A cream is an emulsion (a suspension of one liquid in another) of oil and water. In order to mix oil and water you need an emulsifier. The emulsifiers used in the recipes below are used in the food industry to make bread and vegan ice cream, so are very safe to use on your skin!

If you want to sell creams to the public or to your bodywork clients, here's some good news for you: the highest profits out of all the products in this book are to be made out of creams, anything from 300-1000%. Maybe you have a business here?

CREAM RECIPES

Note: use the double the amount of preservative in the recipes when you use herbal infusions or decocotions instead of boiling spring water. This is because herbal infusions and decoctions naturally contain a lot of bacteria and fungi.

MOISTURISING CREAM FOR DRY/MATURE/SENSITIVE SKIN

Fat Stage (75°-80°C)

6ml Apricot Kernel Oil

3ml Thistle Oil

2g Cetyl Alcohol

2.5g VE Emulsifier

Water Stage (75°-80°C)

4g MF Emulsifier

65ml Boiling Spring Water

2ml/g Glycerine

12 drops Preservative

Third Stage (40°-35°C)

2ml/g NFF Moisturiser

0.5ml/g Vitamin E Oil (undiluted)

Fourth Stage (40°-35°C)

12ml/g Aloe Vera Gel (runny)

Fifth Stage (25°C)

12-15 drops Essential Oil

Vitamin Cream for Sensitive/ Dry/Mature Skin

Fat Stage (75°-80°C)

8ml Peach Kernel Oil

2ml/g Macadamia Nut Oil

2g Cetyl Alcohol

2.5g VE Emulsifier

Water Stage (75°-80°C)

4g MF Emulsifier

55ml Boiling Spring Water

2ml/g Glycerine

12 drops Preservative

Third Stage (40°-35°C)

2ml/g NFF Moisturiser

5ml Evening Primrose Oil

2ml/g Vitamin E Oil (undiluted)

1ml/g Vitamin A Palmitate

1ml/g Sea Buckthorn CO_2 Extract

Fourth Stage (40°-35°C)

13ml/g Aloe Vera Gel (runny)

Fifth Stage (25°C)

12-15 drops Essential Oil

Basic Method for Making a Cream

1. **Fat Stage:** Heat the fat stage ingredients in a double boiler until all of the ingredients have melted and the temperature has risen to 75-80°C. There is no need to use a whisk at this stage.

2. **Water Stage:** After boiling the spring water in a kettle, measure it according to the recipe and pour it over the other water stage raw materials, which you have put into a separate double boiler.

3. Whisk the water stage ingredients well together, making sure that the MF emulsifier powder is fully dissolved in the water and that you don't have any lumps. Then allow the mixture to heat to 75-80°C.

4. When both fat and water stages are over 75°C (check with a thermometer), remove both double boilers from the hob, keeping the water stage mixture hot by leaving it on the top half of the double boiler.

5. Now pour the melted fat stage into the water stage in a thin, steady stream, while continuously whisking the mixture from side to side for 5 minutes. If necessary, use a spatula to scrape the mixture from the sides of the saucepan (or bowl).

6. Allow the mixture to cool, stirring all the time. You can speed up by the cooling process by replacing the hot water in the double boiler with very COLD water. In the process of cooling down, the mixture becomes a cream and will reach its thickest consistency when it is has cooled down to room temperature.

7. **Third Stage:** Stir in the third stage ingredients when the mixture has cooled to under 40°C.

8. **Fourth Stage:** Stir in the aloe vera gel. **Note**: The aloe vera gel makes the cream fluffier and so softer and smoother on the skin. Use the recipe for making gels *(see page 48)*.

9. **Fifth Stage:** Continue stirring until the mixture has cooled to under 25°C, then thoroughly mix in the essential oils.

10. Pour the cream into one big jar or smaller jars and label.

Tips for Making Creams

⚹ To make effective anti-wrinkle creams, you can add one or two extra ingredients during the third stage of making a cream, such as hyaluronic acid (1%), coenzyme Q10 (0.5-2%) or Remodelling Intense (2%). *(See the Glossary for descriptions of these ingredients.)*

⚹ To ensure a smooth cream, use an electric blender to blend the ingredients for 1 minute after adding the fat stage to the water stage, then continue whisking, as directed in the Method, for 4 more minutes.

⚹ When whisking or stirring, it is important to touch the bottom of the saucepan, or bowl, with the whisk so as not to introduce air into the mixture.

⚹ As you are making a whole litre of cream, you don't need to add the essential oils to the whole amount straight away; you can add essential oils when putting the cream into smaller jars.

⚹ Shelf life of these creams is 1.5-2 years.

⚹ Practising aromatherapists can combine the creams with essential oils and other ingredients suited to the special needs of their clients.

⚹ You can also make a lotion using these cream recipes by whisking in a quantity of water equal to the amount of cream. So, to clarify, if you have a 100ml of ready-made cream, you whisk in, little by little, up to 100ml of cold spring water until you reach a consistency you like for your lotion. For each 10ml of water you add, you will need to add 1 drop of the preservative you are using, so in our example you need to mix in an extra 10 drops of preservative.

ESSENTIAL OILS

ESSENTIAL OILS

USING ESSENTIAL OILS SAFELY

POPULAR ESSENTIAL OILS & ABSOLUTES

Essential oils enhance the useful properties of your spa products and make them smell good too! They can stimulate, calm, heal, energise; whatever is needed. The oils have measurable biological effects and the right fragrance can set the right mood for your spa treatments or for the customers and friends using your products. This section includes safety advice and a short guide to some of the more popular essential oils. Enjoy!

USING ESSENTIAL OILS SAFELY

When using essential oils it is very important to adhere to the recommended dosage to achieve the desired effect. The wrong dosage (which is often the temptation to use too much) can result in skin damage, headache, nausea or similar. Some essential oils are not suitable for use during pregnancy or in conjunction with high blood pressure, while some should be used sparingly on the skin. See directions for individual oils.

The ancient Greeks and Romans endowed Rosemary with sacred status for its many beneficial uses...

...but it should be used with care by those with high blood pressure, and not at all during pregnancy or in conjunction with homoeopathic treatment...

Popular Essential Oils & Absolutes

In this section you will find information on some popular essential oils and absolutes that can be used in your spa products.

List of Essential Oils

Bay Leaf *(laurus nobilis)*

Parts used: Leaf

Perfume: Herbaceous, round, green aroma, smelling of the woods and slightly minty. Classic men's aftershave scent.

Used in spa products: As an antiseptic for oily skin and acne and for strengthening hair.

Safety information: Use with care, it may be irritating to the skin. Do not use during pregnancy.

Benzoin *(styrax tonkinensis)*
Parts used: Resin

Perfume: Warm, well-rounded, soft aroma with a touch of vanilla.

Used in spa products: As an antiseptic treatment for chapped, dry, and cracked skin. Excellent for warming the sore or tired muscles.

Safety information: If added to the bath, only use 2 drops per bath. May not be suitable during pregnancy.

Black Pepper *(piper nigrum)*
Parts used: Flowers

Perfume: Crisp, fresh, peppercorn aroma.

Used in spa products: For treating aching muscles, arthritis, circulation, sluggish digestion.

Safety information: Can be irritating to the skin in high doses.

Bergamot *(citrus bergamia)*

Parts used: Peel

Perfume: Sweet citrus aroma with a floral/fruity undertone.

Used in spa products: For oily skin and acne.

Safety information: Increases the skin's sensitivity to sunlight.

Cedarwood *(cedrus atlantica)*

Parts used: Wood

Perfume: Soft, round, sweet, woody, resiny aroma.

Used in spa products: As an astringent on oily skin; an antiseptic on acne.

Safety information: Use with care, it may be irritating to the skin. May not be suitable during pregnancy.

CLOVES (eugenia caryophyllus)

Parts used: Flowers/buds

Perfume: Deep, very warm and spicy aroma.

Used in spa products: For its antiseptic qualities. Not commonly used for treating acne but can be used for this purpose. Used in men's aftershave products.

Safety information: Very irritating to the skin. Must be used in concentrations of less than 1% in Vegetable Oil and even less in other products. Do not use in Baths.

CYPRESS (cupressus sempervirens)

Parts used: Needles

Perfume: Smell of needles, with a herbaceous, woody, resiny tone.

Used in spa products: Astringent, good for oily skin and skin with broken capillaries. Good for cellulite - tightens up the skin, diuretic.

GERANIUM (pelargonium graveolens)

Parts used: Leaves

Perfume: Mixture of rose and citrus aroma, quite direct and slightly green.

Used in spa products: Excellent mood balancer for women and for treating cellulite, so excellent for

Facial Steam Baths, Foot or Whole Body Baths, and Massage Oils and Creams. Also stabilises production of sebum (oil from glands in the skin). Suitable for oily and dry skin.

GINGER (zingiber officinale)

Parts used: Root

Perfume: Strong ginger smell with spicy, sharp, warm and energising notes.

Used in spa products: Good muscle warming oil for massage oil blends. Also good for treating aches and pains, as well as poor circulation and arthritic pain. Add sparingly to baths and compresses. Use in facial steam baths for coughs and colds.

Safety information: Use with care; this Oil may irritate the skin or mucous membrane. When adding this Oil to bath products, add only the equivalent of 1-2 drops per bath.

GRAPEFRUIT (citrus paradisi)

Parts used: Peel

Perfume: Slightly sour but refreshing citrus aroma with a bitter touch.

Used in spa products: For treating oily skin and acne and helps to break down cellulite. Also stimulates hair growth.

Safety information: Increases the skin's sensitivity to sunlight.

JASMINE (ABSOLUTE) (jasmin grandifolium)

Parts used: Flowers

Perfume: Hypnotically sweet, floral aroma with a hint of green and herbs. Be careful with dosage, as its smell can be very dominant.

Used in spa products: For sensitive and very dry skin.

Safety information: Dose with care. Can be suffocating and irritating to the skin if dosage is too high. Do not use if pregnant.

LAVENDER *(lavandula angustifolia)*

Parts used: Flowers

Perfume: Typical lavender aroma, floral, herbaceous and green.

Used in spa products: For relaxing and soothing properties. Good for all skin types including mature, sunburnt and irritated skin and skin with acne.

LEMON *(citrus limonum)*

Parts used: Peel

Perfume: Fresh, sweet and sour citrus aroma with a touch of green.

Used in spa products: For its very antiseptic and refreshing properties. Good for oily skin and acne. Helps to break down cellulite.

Safety information: Increases the skin's sensitivity to sunlight.

MANDARIN *(citrus reticulata)*

Parts used: Peel

Perfume: Soft, warm, kind citrus aroma with slightly floral fragrance.

Used in spa products: In skin toners for all skin types. Excellent for young children or the elderly – you could it to baths or facial steams.

Safety information: Increases the skin's sensitivity to sunlight.

NEROLI *(citrus aurantium)*

Parts used: Peel

Perfume: Very warm, floral and slightly fruity aroma.

Used in spa products: For its relaxing and uplifting properties. Good for mature skin, broken capillaries, sensitive and dry skin.

ORANGE *(citrus sinensis)*

Parts used: Peel

Perfume: Sweet, warm, citrus. Goes well with most other fragrances.

Used in spa products: For its uplifting and relaxing qualities. Also for mature skin, swollen skin or acne and Foot Creams for dissolving hard skin.

Safety information: Increases the skin's sensitivity to sunlight.

PATCHOULI *(pogostemon patchouli)*

Parts used: Leaves

Perfume: Earthy, soft aroma.

Used in spa products: For its astringent properties. Use for chapped and cracked skin, oily and mature skin. Tightens up tired, loose skin.

PETITGRAIN *(citrus aurantium)*

Parts used: Leaves

Perfume: Warm, slightly over-ripe citrus aroma with a hint of flowers.

Used in spa products: For oily and dry skin, can in Skin Toners, Creams, Lotions, Facial Steam Baths and Foam Baths. Excellent for stress relief.

PEPPERMINT *(mentha piperita)*

Parts used: Leaves

Perfume: Cooling, direct, lively, invigorating scent. Be careful with dosage as it can be very dominant.

Used in spa products: For its cooling, refreshing and uplifting qualities. Excellent for cooling foot gels.

Safety information: Use with care. Can cause itching when used in concentrations higher than 1%. Only 1 drop is recommended for use in baths. Do not use in conjunction with homoeopathic remedies as it can act as an antidote.

ROSE DE MAI (ABSOLUTE) *(rosa centifolia)*

Parts used: Flowers

Perfume: Very floral, slightly citrus and spicy.

Used in spa products: For dry and mature skin as well as for broken capillaries. Excellent for stress relief and a favourite with women.

ROSEMARY *(rosmarinus officinalis)*

Parts used: Leaves

Perfume: Herbaceous, spicy, stimulating, minty aroma. Be careful with dosing, as it can be very dominant.

Used in spa products: For its stimulating, invigorating, warming and refreshing properties. Circulation promoting in the skin and anti-cellulite. Good for oily skin and acne as well as small amounts of dry and mature skin.

Safety information: Do not use when pregnant or in conjunction with homoeopathic treatment. Use with care where there is high blood pressure.

SANDALWOOD MYSORE *(santalum album)*

Parts used: Wood

Perfume: Sweet, sensual, warm, woody smell.

Used in spa products: For dry and sensitive skin and as an antiseptic for acne. Great for a relaxing and harmonising Spa treatment.

TEA TREE *(melaleuca alternifolia)*

Parts used: Leaves

Perfume: Cleansing, herbaceous and slightly woody aroma.

Used in spa products: Use for acne, sunburn, fungal infections, psoriasis, sweaty feet, insect bites, etc.

VETIVERT *(adropogonis zizanoides)*

Parts used: Root

Perfume: Juicy, earthy, smoky aroma with a sweet undertone. Good for men's eau de colognes as well as a base oil for earthy feminine blends.

Used in spa products: Very relaxing, strengthening the nervous system. For mature skin, astringent and softening with chapped and cracked skin.

YLANG YLANG *(cananga odorata genuina)*

Parts used: Flowers

Perfume: Floral, exotic, slightly banana scented, narcotic aroma.

Used in spa products: Stabilises production of sebum (oil from glands in the skin), so excellent for oily skin and acne. Very uplifting and relaxing.

GLOSSARY

A

ACTIVE HEATING MUD

Active Heating Muds often combine marine mud (sea silt), clay, seaweeds and algae such as spirulina. Active heating mud is used in body wraps or face masks as well as added to other spa products such exfoliants and scrubs for their detoxing and revitalising effects.

AHA NATURAL FRUIT ACIDS

A natural, mild peeling agent. Includes 12-17% Glycolic Acid. A natural source of AHAs (Alpha Hydroxy Acids) from botanical extracts. Natural fruit AHAs are extracted from fruits and other botanicals such as sugar cane. AHAs have been shown to promote smoother, younger looking skin by increasing the rate of cell renewal and have excellent moisturising properties.

Note: Never use around the eyes and do a skin sensitivity test on a patch of skin if you are a first-time user of any AHA product.

ALOE VERA CONCENTRATE

A liquid concentrate made from the *aloe barbadensis* plant. The one in the recipes has a 1:9, i.e. 100ml of the Concentrate added to 900ml of water and other ingredients makes 1 litre of Aloe Vera Gel. It can also be added to spa products without first making it into a gel.

ALOE VERA GEL

A skin gel which has the plant *aloe barbadensis* as its main ingredient.

APRICOT KERNEL OIL
[INCI name: Prunus armeniaca]

A softening and stable oil which is especially suitable for sensitive, dry and mature skin. The oil is semi-fatty and is easily absorbed by the skin. It is recommended that you buy cold pressed apricot kernel oil.

AROMAS

Refers to natural aromas produced from organic raw materials with an alcohol content of approximately 15%, stocked by Aromantic. These are great fragrances for all kinds of water-based spa products such as skin toners, foam baths, creams, lotions, baths, etc. You can also use them in fat-based products such as body butters and ointments. The results will vary when used in oil-only products. They have a wonderful taste and can be used in foods such as sweets, deserts, puddings, ice creams and drinks.

AVOCADO BUTTER
[INCI name: Persea gratissima]

Produced from avocado pulp, avocado butter can be added to spa products such as creams, sun creams, lotions and massage oils. Mild, nourishing and excellent for dry skin patches. Melting point 30°C to 35°C, so melts in contact with your skin.

AVOCADO OIL
[INCI name: Persea gratissima]

Avocado oil is a mild, nourishing, semi-fatty oil, rich in vitamins. It is used is used in spa products for treating skin that is dry, tired and lacks lustre.

B

BASE FOAM BATH
[INCI: Aqua (Still Water); Mipa-Laureth Sulphate, Laureth 4, Cocoamide DEA (Bath Foam Emulsifier); Benzyl Alcohol, Phenoxyethanol and Potassium Sorbate (Preservative K); Lactic Acid (Vegan)]

Refers to an Aromantic product, a natural foam bath made from mainly coconut-based detergent. You can your favourite essential oils to the base foam bath and then use in the bath. The foam bath helps to disperse the essentials oils throughout the whole bath, not just on the surface, avoiding skin irritations. *Also see Foam Bath Emulsifier.*

BEESWAX
[INCI name: Cera flava]

A bee product usually sold in thin sheets, although organic beeswax is often sold in lumps. Either way, it is melted down and added to ointments, lip balms and lipsticks to give them consistency. Make sure you buy pure either organic beeswax or pure beeswax from areas such as parts of Sweden where the bees have not been affected by the varroa mite.

BETA DETERGENT
[INCI name: Cocoamidopropyl betaine/NAC]

Betaine occurs naturally in sugar beet but is mainly extracted from coconut butter and then transformed into a detergent with the help of chemicals and is very gentle on the skin. Considered a secondary or help detergent, it is often used in combination with other detergents to make them milder and it produces a fine foam.

BICARBONATE OF SODA
[INCI name: Sodium bicarbonate]

Also known as baking soda, bread soda or sodium bicarbonate, bicarbonate of soda is a soluble white crystalline chemical compound, with a slight alkaline taste. It is found in many mineral springs and also produced artificially. In making spa products it is used for its alkalising properties in baths and bath salts and to make fizzy bath bombs and in baths and bath salts.

BISABOLOL
[INCI name: Bisabolol, Jojoba Wax]

Derived from german chamomile, bisabolol is a naturally occurring versatile active ingredient for the cosmetics industry and has been used in traditional medicine in Europe for hundreds of years. It is used in spa products for its well-documented calming action on sensitive skin.

BLUE AZULENE COLOUR
[INCI name: Matricaria recutita]

A natural blue colour derived from german chamomile used to impart a transparent blue colour to spa products.

BORAGE OIL
[INCI name: Borago officinalis]

A dry, thin oil with an exceptionally high content (20-24%) of gamma linolenic acid (GLA), a substance the body needs to create 'good' prostaglandins. As a spa product, it is excellent in anti-wrinkle oil blends and serums and eye contour products. It is good for all skin types, except maybe sensitive skin (use evening primrose oil instead) but works particularly well for mature and dry skin.

BOTANICAL CO_2 EXTRACTS

These botanical extracts are extracted with CO_2 gas (carbon dioxide), which is the purest and gentlest way of making concentrated herbal extracts without the use of either heat or solvents. They are very concentrated as these are full extractions, which include the essential oils as well as the fat-soluble and water-soluble substances from the plants. CO_2 extracts are added to spa products for their individual therapeutic benefits.

C

CALENDULA CO_2 EXTRACT
[INCI name: Calendula officinalis]

Also known as Marigold CO_2 Extract, it is known for its healing properties and so is often used in products for sensitive skin or in sun products.

CAMELINA OIL
[INCI name: Camelina sativa]

A very dry, thin, short oil, which feels rather rough on the skin so it is important to always blend it with softer oils. Due to its high content of omega 3 up to 45%, can be taken internally as a vegetarian alternative to marine oils although it is not equivalent to marine oils and chia seed oil does not contain EPA (eicosopentaenoic acid) or DHA (docosahexaeonoic acid), which are both found in cold water fish oils. As a spa product, it is excellent in anti-wrinkle oil blends and serums, eye contour products, face oils, body oils, as part of a massage oil blend, creams, lotions, etc. The oil is also known as 'gold of pleasure' or 'wild flax'.

CARBAMIDE CRYSTALS
[INCI name: Urea]

A moisturiser synthesised from ammonia and carbon dioxide. It is added to spa products for its moisturising and antiseptic purposes.

CARRAGEEN
[INCI: Carrageenan]

Carrageen is a dark purple edible sea-weed (algae), also known as Irish Moss, found on the rocky north Atlantic coasts of Europe and North America. Containining a wide range of minerals, vitamins and trace elements, it is used in spa products for its detoxifying and nourishing properties.

CAROTENE

Is a botanical extract usually diluted in vegetable oil to make it pourable. It is added to spa products to help combat dry and tired skin. It can also be used as a natural colouring both for products and the skin.

CASTOR OIL
[INCI name: Ricinus communis]

This is a viscous oil with a high fat content, which is absorbed by the skin very slowly. Especially good in cleansing and exfoliating spa products, as well as massage oils.

CETYL ALCOHOL

Used as a stabiliser for emulsifiers. Aromantic's cetyl alcohol is made from palm kernel oil fatty acid (palmitic acid), which is treated with liquid gas so that the free oxygen (O) atom is removed. Cetyl alcohol makes creams and lotions firmer and gives them consistency.

CHIA SEED OIL
[INCI name: Salvia hispanica]

Thin, dry and very soft, it has a silky soft skin feeling & a pleasant smell. Chia seed oil has a very similar omega 3 & 6 content to kiwi seed oil, but is much cheaper to buy (about one-third). Due to the high content of omega 3, we recommend that you buy chia seed oil that has an added antioxidant such as vitamin E oil to secure a shelf life of 2 years. You can use chia seed oil in the same way as kiwi seed oil: it soothes fine wrinkles and improves skin elasticity, so add the oil to serums, creams & lotions for these purposes. It also soothes the cost of any anti-wrinkle blend! It is good for treating acne-prone, oily and large-pored skin. As it is so silky & soft, it is excellent for sensitive skin too. Because of its high omega 3 (ALA) content - up to 63% - chia seed oil can be taken internally as a vegetarian alternative to marine oils although it is not equivalent to marine oils and chia seed oil does not contain EPA (eicosopentaenoic acid) or DHA (docosahexaeonoic acid), which are both found in cold water fish oils.

CITRIC ACID
[INCI name: Citric acid]

This acid can be produced naturally from lemons but most of it is produced synthetically. It is used as an acidity/pH regulator in spa products so those products maintain the natural acid balance of the skin.

CLAY
[INCI name: Clay]

Clay is rich in minerals and active enzymes and has a long tradition of use in natural medicine in many parts of the world for its many healing benefits. Different coloured clays such as green, pink, red, yellow, and white are used to treat different conditions and are mixed with water or herbal infusions and other active ingredients for use in spa products.

CITRIC ACID AND CELLULOSE
[INCI name: Citric acid, Hydroxyethylcellulose]

Used to make fizzy bath bombs together with Sodium Bicarbonate.

COCOA BUTTER
[INCI name: Theobroma cacao]

Derived from the cocoa bean found on the cocoa tree, a tropical evergreen grown in South America and Africa. Gives softness, nourishment, protection and consistency to spa products. It is mild and most people tolerate it well.

COCONUT BUTTER
[INCI name: Cocos nucifera]

Extracted from Coconuts grown on palm trees and used for making body butters. It also adds body when melted into massage oil blends. It is mild and most people tolerate it well. You can also get aroma-retained coconut butter, which has a gorgeous smell.

COCONUT OIL, LIQUID FRACTIONATED
[INCI name: Cocos nucifera]

The solid fatty acids have been removed from the coconut fat so it becomes liquid. Adds body and good lubricating and softening properties to spa products.

COENZYME Q10
[INCI name: Ubiquinone]

Coenzyme Q_{10} is naturally present in the skin with higher levels in the epidermis/horny layer than the dermis. The sebum is particularly rich in these lipophilic antioxidants to protect the outer skin surface from oxidative attack. However it has also been shown that the level Coenzyme Q_{10} declines with age. After topical application of Q10 plus E, skin enzymes will release the active antioxidants tocopherol and ubiquinol, helping to balance the skin's antioxidant level. Coenzyme Q_{10} together with vitamin E is even more effective.

COLOURS

There are a variety of colours that can be used to make spa products. Make sure that you use the type appropriate to the products. You can get professional water and non-water based colours and shimmering pearlescent colours. It is also safe to use artificial or natural food colours, but these generally fade faster than the professional colours, particularly if your product is exposed to light. **Note**: a small minority of people are allergic to food colours, even though they are safe to eat for most of us. Check with your clients or friends and family first before adding these to your products.

COMFREY OIL

This is a macerated oil, the colour of deep green because of the allantoin content in comfrey. It also contains Tannins, Glycosides and is an excellent source of B12, so very appropriate in Creams for vegetarians and vegans who are short of this essential Vitamin. It also contains a vegetable protein and is cell proliferant, rebuilding damaged cells. In Creams, it can repair damage caused by surgery, acne, or eczema and is an essential Vegetable Oil for your healing preparations. In Cream and Lotion preparations for athletes, it aids torn muscles, ligaments and strains. In preparations for mature women, it assists in the treatment and prevention of osteoporosis.

CORNFLOUR

Used as a thickening agent in spa products, cornflour, also known as cornstarch, is the gluten-free starch, which has been extracted from maize (Indian corn). It is A fine, white powder, which sometimes has a yellowish tinge. Not to be confused with cornmeal, which Americans sometimes call cornflour.

D

DEAD SEA SALT
[INCI name: Sodium chloride]

Dead Sea salt exfoliates and revitalises the skin and helps to draw out toxins. It is well known for its ability to relieve aches and pains, reduce stiffness after exertion, relax the muscles and relieve skin problems. However, it is no longer sustainable to harvest Dead Sea salt so I suggest that you use ordinary sea salt instead.

DECOCTIONS, HERBAL

Herbal decoctions are sometimes used in the recipes to make various spa products. When using horsetail, or the tougher parts of a plant like the roots, seeds, berries or the bark of a plant, make a decoction rather than an infusion (see 'Infusions, Herbal'). Making a decoction involves boiling the herbs. Put around 2-3g or more of the dried, or 20-30g of the fresh, herb parts into 100ml of water and cover the saucepan. Bring the mixture to a boil and continue to boil for about twenty minutes. You may need to add a bit more water if steam escapes. Steep and strain the mixture and use according to the method in the recipe. When making decoctions do not use an aluminium pan; instead use a stainless steel, glass, ceramic or enamel (make sure it's not chipped, though) pan. When adding decoctions to products, you need to increase the amount of preservative you would normally use from the more usual 0.6%, up to 1% (1ml/g for every 100m/g of product).

D-PANTHENOL
[INCI name: Panthenol]

Added to spa products for the skin and hair. It is a water-soluble, odour-free and a syrupy liquid consisting of 75%

pantothenic acid (provitamin B$_5$) and 25% water. Used in spa products for the skin as it binds the moisture in the surface layers of the skin and it speeds up cell regeneration, soothes itchiness and infections. Used in spa products for nail treatments, skin toners and it gives the hair a protective film that makes it easier to handle.

E

EPSOM SALTS
[INCI name: Magnesium Sulfate]

Crystals that are derived from magnesium sulfate and used in the bath for detoxification and to relieve common aches and pains, especially in the feet or back.

ESSENTIAL OILS

An essential oil, also known as volatile oil or ethereal oil, is an aromatic liquid extracted from the leaves, stems, flowers, and other parts of plants through distillation that have a long tradition of providing a variety of therapeutic benefits. Therapeutic use generally includes dilution of the highly concentrated oil.

EVENING PRIMROSE OIL
[INCI name: Oenothera biennis]

A dry, thin oil with an exceptionally high content (10-12%) of gamma linolenic acid (GLA), an omega 6 fatty acid the body needs to create prostaglandins.

F

FLAXSEED GEL
[INCI name: Linum usitatissimum]

Make flaxseed gel by adding boiling water to whole flax seeds (linseed), leave under lid overnight and strain off in the morning. This can be stored for up to 1 week in a fridge or, if you add 1% preservative, it will last up to 6 months. It is used as a natural gel.

FLOWER WATER (See Hydrolates)

FOAM BATH EMULSIFIER

Refers to an Aromantic product to which 75-80% boiling water and 0.5-1% preservative is added to make a Base Foam Bath *(see under 'B')*.

FUNORI

Known as a delicious addition to miso soup, or salads, this purple Japanese seaweed is used in Spa products to make hair soft and skin clear. It is traditionally used in Japan to remove age spots. It is also used as a hair shampoo and is known as the secret to Japanese women's shiny, beautiful hair.

G

GLYCERINE
[INCI name: Glycerine]

Glycerine is an alcohol, an oily, thick, odourless, colourless, sweet tasting liquid which is derived from naturally occurring fatty acids, such as coconut. It is used in spa products as a moisturiser that helps to attract, and retain, moisture to the skin and hair as well as improving the spreadability of formulas and their skin and hair softening qualities.

Note: Glycerine can be produced from animal fats or synthetically produced. I recommend that you use only vegetable-based glycerine for your spa products.

GLYCEROL EXTRACT

Glycerol extracts have soothing and moisturising properties as well as other benefits, depending on which plant the extract is made from.

Grape Seed Oil
[INCI name: Vitis vinifera]

This vegetable oil is extracted from the seed of grapes. It is a dry oil with good spreadability on the skin and is best used in combination with fattier and more nutritious vegetable oils for body massage.

H

Hemp Seed Oil
[INCI name: Cannabis sativa]

A very, very dry oil that is rough by it itself on the skin, but is absorbed easily. A good source of Essential Fatty Acids (Omega 3 and 6). Use in different spa products for or normal, large-pored or oily skin.

Honey Moisturiser
[INCI name: Hydroxypropyltrimomium honey]

Honey Moisturiser is chemically altered honey, which has a low viscosity and is a clear, almost colourless liquid, which has soothing, strengthening and moisturising properties and a pleasant feel on the skin and hair. It has excellent moisture-binding properties, with twice the moisturising ability of glycerine. Honey moisturiser is added to spa products to moisturise the hair, help to repair split ends and to penetrate the endocuticle region in the nails.

Hyaluronic Acid
[INCI name: varies according to source]

Hyaluronic acid is what gives the skin its volume and fullness. It is one of the chief components of the extracellular skin matrix and it contributes significantly to cell proliferation. Aging can result in the loss of hyaluronic acid, which in turn results in skin that has less volume and the formation of wrinkles and folds. Its hydrating properties result in increased skin smoothness, softening and decreased wrinkles. Its rejuvenating properties result in increased skin smoothness and softness. It also protects the cell structure and defending against external threats and bacterial infections. It also exhibits viscous flow, elastic and pseudoplastic properties. This property is unique to HA. It is popularly called "The Fountain of Youth", hyaluronic acid and it is a common ingredient in skin care products. Make sure that you buy Hyaluronic Acid that is made by producing enzymes from a bacteria-based biofermermentation process and and not sourced from poultry (roosters' combs).

Hydrolate

Hydrolates, also known as herbal and floral waters, or hydrosols, are by-products of the process of making essential oils. These waters can sometimes be used, as they are, as skin toners, facial cleansers, face masks, hair rinses, for aromatic baths, baby baths, on compresses or in sprays for freshening up the skin. Different hydrolates e.g. rose, orange blossom, or witch hazel are used in spa products for their particular properties to replace, or partially replace, water in various spa products along with other ingredients.

I

INCI name

The International Nomenclature of Cosmetic Ingredients, abbreviated INCI, is a system of names for waxes, oils, pigments, chemicals, and other ingredients of soaps, cosmetics, and the like, based on scientific names and other Latin and English words. INCI names often differ greatly from

systematic chemical nomenclature or from more common trivial names.
Source: Wikipedia

Infusions, Herbal

Herbal infusions are sometimes used in the recipes to make various spa products. An Infusion is made like a tea. If using a herbal infusion instead of boiling water in your recipe, make it as follows: Allow 2-3g dried herbs per 100ml water (please note that sometimes the amount of dried herb used will vary according to strength needed). Pour boiling water over the herbs. Cover and allow to stand for 10-20 minutes. Strain and use according to the method in the recipe. When adding infusions to products, you need to increase the amount of preservative you would normally use from the more usual 0.6%, up to 1% (1ml/g for every 100m/g of product).

J

Jojoba Exfoliating Grains

Refers to an Aromantic product. Extracted from the waxes of the jojoba plant, with or without added colour. The grains are smooth and do not irritate the skin. The fine grain size is excellent for exfoliating dead skin and improving circulation. You can also add the grains after you've made your products or to other ready-made products. You may also substitute the jojoba exfoliating grains with a similar product.

Jojoba Oil
[Simmondsia chinensis]

Actually a liquid wax, which feels dry. It softens, protects and helps the skin to hold its moisture. Also good as a hair oil and adds protection to hand creams. It can be used for all skin types and very good for whole body massage.

K

Kaolin
[INCI name: Kaolin]

Also called aluminium silicate, white clay or china clay, kaolin is a soft mineral in the form of fine-grained white clay, which is refined. It is used in spa products such: as in face masks to absorb excess fats and to tone up the skin; as a mild abrasive agent in peeling creams; in absorptive clay-based ointments; and also in sunscreen products.

Note: For cosmetics, one should only use pharmaceutical-grade kaolin.

Kiwi Seed Oil
[INCI name: Actinidia deliciosa]

An unique oil as it contains a very high level of omega 3 fatty acids (up to 65%) and other micro nutrients. Skin studies have shown that it improves skin condition & protects against moisture loss. Has an excellent after-feel & absorbs easily making it the perfect ingredient in spa products such as face creams & hair conditioning creams. It is a soft & smooth oil, making it suitable for sensitive skin.

Kombu

An edible wide, thick, dark green seaweed which grows in deep ocean water. Used in Japanese cooking. Used as a spa product for moisturising baths.

L

Lactic Acid
[INCI name: Lactic Acid]

One of the most regularly occurring acids in nature, lactic acid and its salts have a preservative effect as certain bacteria do not thrive in an acid environment. It is used primarily to help the skin to re-balance its own natural acidity level and so added to spa skin care products that are used after cleansers and soap, such as toners and creams and lotions. It is also used in soaps for use on the body and for intimate hygiene.

M

MACADAMIA NUT OIL
[INCI name: Macadamia tetraphylla]

A very fatty oil which is soft and nice to use. Despite its fattiness, it is readily absorbed by the skin and is especially good to use for mature and dry skin as well as skin which has difficulty retaining its moisture.

MANGO BUTTER
[INCI name: Mangifera indica L]

Produced from mango seed kernels, mango butter adds excellent moisturising and lubricating properties to spa products such as body butters, ointments, creams, lotions and lip balms. Also very good for moisturising dry patches on chapped skin.

MF EMULSIFIER

Refers to an Aromantic product. A vegetable-based emulsifier for creams and lotions, which amateurs and professionals alike will find extremely easy to use. Derived from lactic acid and vegetable-based stearic acid, it produces a professional cosmetic product. MF needs to be used in combination with VE Emulsifier. Both MF and VE are both used as Emulsifiers to make vegan ice cream in the Scandinavian food industry. This shows that they are both very safe emulsifiers to use as they are edible.

N

NEROLI HYDROLATE

See Orange Blossom Hydrolate.

NFF MOISTURISER

An Aromantic product, which is a natural, vegetable-based moisturising factor added to skin toners, creams and lotions to bind moisture deeper into the epidermis. It can add 60-70% more moisture.

O

OLIVE OIL
[INCI name: Olea europea]

A fatty to half-fatty oil, which is good for mature or dry skin. Blend it with thistle or sunflower if it feels too fatty. It is used on its own or in blends for spa. It is best to use a high quality cold pressed and extra virgin oil for skin care.

OMEGA 3

Omega 3 is the name given to a family of polyunsaturated fatty acids, which are important in human nutrition and for the skin. These are found in various quantities in various vegetable oils, which are used as, or in, spa products for their benefits to the skin. The most important omega 3 fatty acid is alpha linolenic acid (ALA), which is an essential fatty acid.

OMEGA 6

Omega 6 is the name given to a family of duounsaturated fatty acids, which are important in human nutrition and for the skin. These are found in various quantities in various vegetable oils, which are used as, or in, spa products for their benefits to the skin. The most important omega 6 fatty acid is linoleic acid (LA), which is an essential fatty acid.

P

Palm Kernel Oil
[INCI name: Elaeis guineensis]

This is a solid white, very fatty and soft wax, which is derived from the kernel of the oil palm *Elaeis guineensis*. It can be used to add moisturising and protecting properties to spa products, such as body butters. It is often used in soaps, as it saponifies easily.

Peach Kernel Oil
[INCI name: Prunus persica]

A semi-fatty oil that has the same properties as apricot kernel oil. Used in spa products for sensitive, dry and mature skin.

Potato flour
[INCI name: Potato flour]

Used for making basic powders for various make-up products, such as rouge, eye shadow, etc. and used in spa products as a thickening agent.

Preservative

Preservatives are used to inhibit the destructive activities of microorganisms in products containing water, herbal infusions, or herbal decoctions. You can use different types that are on the market.

Propylene glycol
[INCI name: Propylene glycol]

I would recommend using propylene glycol as a moisturiser in fizzy bath bombs as it contains no water and that is necessary for these products. I do not recommend it's use in any other products.

Q

Q10 plus E

Refers to an Aromantic product. Coenzyme Q10 and vitamin E are the most important lipophilic (oil-loving) skin antioxidants. Both, structurally closely related to each other, are naturally contained in almost every body cell including the skin. Q10 plus E is a specially designed combination of coenzyme Q10 and vitamin E acetate for personal care skin regeneration, anti-aging and protection formulations.

R

Remodelling Intense

Refers to an Aromantic product, which has been proven to restructure, firm and smooth the face and body. It is a 100% natural, plant-derived ingredient, an oily extract of Spilanthes acmella, which is cultivated in South Africa by a cooperative of local farmers. The buds of the flower are collected to produce the extract, and the plant remains unharmed in the process.

Remodelling Intense is preservative- and glycols-free, in a base of Capric/Caprylic Triglycerides, the same as Liquid Fractionated Coconut Oil.

Rice Bran Oil
[INCI name: Oryza sativa]

A half-fatty to half-dry oil traditionally used in Japan. Used in spa products for its mild and softening properties on the skin. A good source of omega 6 fatty acid.

Rosehip Seed CO_2 Extract

CO_2 Extracts are extracted from the botanical material with CO_2 gas (carbon dioxide). This is currently the purest and gentlest way of making botanical extracts without the use of either heat or solvents. Rosehip CO_2 extract contains a high content of both vitamin A and omega 3 fatty acid and is used in spa products that treat sensitive skin.

ROSEHIP OIL
[INCI name: Rosa rubginosa]

A dry to very dry oil and the only vegetable oil, which contains natural retinoic acid (vitamin A acid). It is used in Spa products for treating oily skin, sensitive skin, skin problems and skin with large pores. It is also an excellent vegetable oil source of omega 3 essential fatty acid and a good source of omega 6.

ROSEMARY CO_2 EXTRACT

A CO_2 Extract, which is an antioxidant also. Antioxidants are important additives in spa formulations for increasing their shelf life. This is important if you want to sell your products to the public, family or friends. This antioxidant is more stable than vitamin E for products such as vegetable oils and creams. It is also added to spa products that have a high quantity of vitamin E in them as the rosemary CO_2 extract helps slow down the oxidation process of the vitamin E.

S

SEA SALT
[INCI name: Sodium chloride]

Salt is excellent for the use as bath salts (rough grained) in detoxifying baths or as a scrubbing/exfoliating agent (fine grained).

SEA BUCKTHORN
[INCI name: Hippophae rhamnoides]

Sea buckthorn CO_2 extract alleviates sunburn, promotes cell rejuvenation, has excellent pain- and stress- relieving and anti-inflammatory properties.

SEA SILK

Refers to an Aromantic product. A good alternative to the animal-based protein extracted from silkworms, Aromantic's sea silk is a marine vegetable, which provides protein enrichment and a silky feeling to spa products such as skin toners, creams and also silk shampoos. It forms a protective and moisturising film on the skin and it soothes the scalp. Especially good for sensitive skin.

SEAWEED

Different types of dried seaweed are used for spa treatments for different therapeutic effects but generally they are high in minerals and can help to tone, moisturise and detox the skin. All types of seaweed stimulate the blood circulation, soften tight muscles and soothe the pain associated with skin irritation and sunburn. When buying seaweeds for baths it is easiest to get carrageen, kombu, wakame or funori. The last three are seaweeds from Japan that you can usually find in your local health food shop.

SESAME OIL
[INCI name: Sesamum indicum]

A half-fatty to half-dry Oil. It has good skin care properties for sun oils as it naturally contains sun protection factor of 2-3 in the oil. Used safely for baby and adult body massage.

SHEA BUTTER
[INCI name: Butyrospermum parkii]

Derived from the stones of the fruit of the shea butter tree, which grows wild in west Africa. Used in spa products for moisturising, protecting and healing the skin, especially dry and damaged skin. It contains 5-10% phytosterol, which stimulates cell growth.

SHEA BUTTER OIL
[INCI name: Butyrospermum parkii]

A very fatty oil that is used in spa products to protect the skin against dehydration and has a natural Sun Protection Factor (SPF) of 2-3. Contains phytosterol, which stimulates the formation and growth of new cells.

SKIN LIGHTENER
[INCI name: Aqua, Glycerine, Extracts of Malva sylvestris, Mentha piperita, Primula veris, Alchemilla vulgaris, Veronica officinlis, Melisa officinalis, Achillea millefolium]

Refers to a fully natural plant derivative and preservative free skin lightener stocked by Aromantic. Up to 5% of the liquid product is added to spa formulations under 60°C for its skin lightening and age-spot reduction effects. If adding to a cream you can add it in stage 3 (40-35°C). I recommend the use of up to 10% of Aromantic's Vitamin C powder to enhance the skin lightener's effect.

SPRING OR STILL WATER

Spring water is a natural product that comes from the earth that retains the same properties and as its underground source. If the recipe calls for the use of water, I recommend the use of bottled spring water. I never use tap water to make products.

SUNFLOWER OIL
[INCI name: Helianthus anuus]

A dry oil containing a high level of linoleic acid. It spreads easily and is absorbed relatively quickly by the skin.

SWEET ALMOND OIL
[INCI name: Prunus amygdalus dulcis]

Has a distinctive nutty smell. A classic, mild semi-fatty oil, which spreads nicely and makes the skin soft, smooth and supple. A popular oil for whole body massage because of its excellent lubricating properties. It is used for most skin types.

T

TEA, BLACK
[INCI name: Camellia sinensis]

Black tea is a "true" tea made from leaves more heavily oxidised than the white, green and oolong varieties and also stronger in flavour with higher caffeine content. It is used as a spa product for astringent and antioxidant eye and skin compresses.

TURKEY RED OIL
[INCI name: Sulphated castor oil]

Produced from castor oil, which is saponified with sodium hydroxide. Used primarily for spa bath preparations where it acts as an emulsifier to distribute essential oil evenly in the bath. It is possible to add 5% of your favourite vegetable oil and up to a maximum of 2% of your favourite essential oils to the turkey red oil.

THISTLE OIL
[INCI name: Carthamus tinctorius]

A dry to very dry and thin oil. An excellent source of essential fatty acids (vitamin F) as they make up 80% of the oil content. Particularly high in omega 6. Good for oily skin and large pores and all skin conditions.

TINCTURES, HERBAL

Are herbs extracted in alcohol. They contain fats and water-soluble ingredients and can be used for a variety of healing purposes as well as having astringent and antiseptic properties. Use no more than 10% tincture in facial water or the alcohol will dry out the skin.

V

VE Emulsifier

Refers to an Aromantic product. A vegetable-based emulsifier for creams and lotions, which amateurs and professionals alike will find extremely easy to use. VE Emulsifier is made from coconut oil and palm kernel oil; it produces a professional cosmetic product. Needs to be used in combination with MF Emulsifier. Both MF and VE are both used as Emulsifiers to make vegan ice cream in the Scandinavian food industry. This shows that they are both very safe emulsifiers to use as they are edible.

Vegetable Oil

Extracted from nuts, seeds, fruits, and leaves, different vegetable oils are used as spa products such as skin, facial and massage oils, massage bars, creams, moisturisers, bath products, ointments and body butters.

Vitamin A Palmitate
[INCI name: Retinol palmitate]

Used in spa products for dry and mature skin and for those that treat skin infections. It is added to products while under 40 °C. For daily use, don't use more than a 2% concentration in blends. **NB** High concentrations of Vitamin A should be avoided by pregnant women.

Vitamin E Oil
[INCI name: Tocopherol]

Vitamin E oil is a classic anti-wrinkle ingredient that helps to reproduce new cells as it is an antioxidant for the skin, which protects against the destruction of the connective tissue caused by free radicals. It is used in spa products for these benefits to the skin when used in quantities above 0.5% in your product. In megadoses on the skin, it is safe to use up to 50% undiluted vitamin E oil in your blends and products. When adding more than 2% vitamin E oil to your products, you need to add another antioxidant, such as Rosemary CO_2 extract, to protect the vitamin E. *See Rosemary CO_2 extract on page 127.*

Vitamin E oil can also be used as an antioxidant that prolongs the shelf life of a product. For this purpose, add 0.3-0.5% to the product.

W

Wakame

Wakame is a kelp and is rich in protein, calcium, iodine, magnesium, iron and folate. As a spa product, it is used in a similar way to kombu for bath products.

X

Xanthan Gum
[INCI name: Xanthan Gum]

A polysaccharide, which is produced by fermenting glucose. Used as a thickening agent to make gels for spa products.

INGREDIENTS TO AVOID

Many commonly used high street products contain ingredients that are animal-derived or that may cause allergic or otherwise negative health and skin reactions. These ingredients are often replaceable with vegetarian or more natural ingredients that are kinder to the skin and to the environment. I definitely don't recommend that you use the ingredients listed in the table below when making natural vegetarian-friendly products.

TABLE 13: INGREDIENTS TO AVOID IN SKIN PRODUCTS

INGREDIENT TO AVOID	COMMENTS
Aluminium salts e.g. Aluminium hydroxychloride, Aluminium chlorohydrate Aluminium sulphate, etc.	Blocks pores, linked to Alzheimer's.
Aqueous cream	Paraffin and water in suspension.
BHT	Butylated hydroxytoluene, may be carcinogenic.
Borax	Sodium borate, strong irritant, may be carcinogenic. Used as an emulsifier
Collagen	Often taken from young animals or aborted fetus.
Euxyl K100 (Benzyl Alcohol, Methylchloroisothiazolinone, Methylisothiazolinone)	Same as Kathon CG.
Hyaluronic Acid (poultry-based type)	Make sure that you buy Hyaluronic Acid that is made by producing enzymes from a bacteria-based biofermermation process and not sourced from poultry (roosters' combs).
Isopropyl myristate	Isopropyl myristate can react negatively with triethanolamines.
Kathon CG	Antifreeze and wood preservative Actizide AC. Used as a preservative in creams and lotions. Can cause severe allergic reactions.
Lanolin	Can be contaminated with pesticides from sheep dip e.g. DDT.
Mineral oil	Blocks pores, acts as a barrier, suppresses normal skin functions.

/contd

Ingredient to avoid	Comments
Paraffin/Petroleum products	Lubrication oil in sewing machines, floor wax. Prevents absorption of vitamins, clogs pores, may be carcinogenic.
Sodium Lauryl Sulphate/ Sodium Lauryl Ether Sulphate.	A detergent. Aggresive on the skin. However, used in smaller quantities together with other raw materials, it should be safe for most people's skin.
Spermataceti cetaceum	Obtained from the head of the sperm whale.
Silk Amino Acid	From dead silk worms.
Tallow	Derived from animal fats. Contains heavy metals & pesticides.
Triethanolamine	Petroleum based, very irritating, can be carcinogenic. Used as a stabiliser for emulsifiers by many High Street brands.
Vaseline	Destroys vitamins, may be carcinogenic. Blocks pores.
2-broma-2-nitropropane-1, 3-diol	Causes diarrhoea, headaches, loss of appetite.

RESOURCES

SUPPLIERS OF INGREDIENTS FOR YOUR SPA PRODUCTS

Some of the ingredients for recipes in this book can be obtained from your local supermarket. There are, however, some ingredients that you will need to buy from specialist suppliers. Here are some suggestions. Please check with relevant suppliers for their latest prices, products and/or details.

AROMANTIC NATURAL SKIN CARE
Worldwide mail order

17 Tytler Street

Forres

Moray

IV36 1EL

Scotland

Tel: +44 (0)1309 696900
Fax: +44 (0)1309 696911

www.aromantic.co.uk (UK website)
www.aromantic.com (US website)

NEAL'S YARD REMEDIES
Worldwide mail order

Tel: 0845 262 3145

www.nealsyardremedies.com

G. BALDWIN & CO

171/173 Walworth Road

London

SE17 1RW

England

Tel: +44 (0)20 7703 5550

Fax: +44 (0)20 7252 6264

www.baldwins.co.uk

LABORATORY TESTING OF PRODUCTS

DR EDMUND FOWLES EF CHEMICAL CONSULTING

If you want to sell your products to the general public at fairs, in your shops or on the internet, then you need a safety assessment certificate. Trading Standards (in the UK) can ask to see them at any time and many insuruers will also want to see them. EF Chemical Consulting provide a cost effective assessment service and guide you through the proocess if it's your first time. As an extra service, he can also ensure teh label complies with EU regulations as it's quite confusing for newcomers to the industry.

Tel: +44 (0)1244 351644

edmund@efchemicalconsulting.co.uk
www.efchemicalconsulting.co.uk

INSURANCE SERVICES FOR THERAPISTS MAKING PRODUCTS FOR SALE

INDEPENDENT PROFESSIONAL THERAPISTS INTERNATIONAL (IPTI)

IPTI offer a comprehensive insurance policy for over 220 alternative and complementary therapies and 40 beauty treatments. If you are among those who are qualified within these 260 categories, you can be covered for products up to the value of £10,000 and up to £1,000,000 for Treatment Risk and Public and Product Liability or pay a slightly higher fee for cover for up to £2,000,000.

You need not to sell only to your clients; you can also sell to the public with this insurance. There is also no restriction that you need to follow my recipes exactly, but are free to experiment yourself. This insurance appears to be very flexible.

Tel: 01777 700383

www.iptiuk.com

FEDERATION OF HOLISTIC THERAPISTS (FHT)

FHT will insure you for selling personal care products to the public if you are a member and can prove that you have attended Aromantic Courses (or equivalent). There is an insurance premium, which is additional to membership fees and a restriction on annual turnover.

Therapy Insurance Services (Handling FHT's insurance)

Tel: 023 8062 1550

INSURANCE COVER FOR HOME CRAFTERS (NON-THERAPISTS) MAKING PRODUCTS FOR SALE

IAN W. WALLACE CRAFT INSURANCE

If you are not a therapist, you can use the services of Ian W. Wallace Home-Craft Insurance scheme. You can receive public and product liability insurance for up to one million pounds for a low annual cost. They only insure cosmetic products and there is no upper limit for your turnover. Any treatments you undertake are not insured. The insurance is valid for the UK as well as the Republic of Ireland.

Tel: 0800 919 359

www.craftinsurance.co.uk

PRODUCT LIABILITY, CONTENTS

DAVID BALEN

David Balen has introduced a 'Bridge Insurance'. It covers transit, contents (up to £15,000), buildings, product liability for up to £2million.

Tel: 01684 893006

www.balen.co.uk

LEGAL REQUIREMENTS FOR SELLING TO THE PUBLIC

AROMANTIC COURSE: COMPLYING WITH LEGAL REQUIREMENTS WITH ROBERTO CIAFF

This 1-day London-based course covers all the legal aspects of making your own products and shows you how to set up a proper practice in manufacturing. You receive a CD-Rom and a file with all the technical data that is needed.

AROMANTIC'S SENSITISER LABELLING CALCULATOR

This Excel-based software calculates the chemical constituents in essential oil blends and lets you know which ones to declare on your labels to comply with European Union labelling law.

Aromantic Natural Skin Care

Tel: +44 (0)1309 696900

Fax: +44 (0)1309 696911

www.aromantic.co.uk

BIBLIOGRAPHY

Borseth, Kolbjørn, The Aromantic Guide to making your own Natural Skin, Hair and Body Care products, 2007. ISBN 978-0-9554323-1-6.

Borseth, Kolbjørn, The Aromantic Guide to the use of Herbs in Skin, Hair and Health Care products, 2006. ISBN 978-0-9554323-0-9

Borseth, Kolbjørn, The Aromantic Guide to Unlocking the Powerful Health & Rejuvenation Benefits of Vegetable Oils, 2008. ISBN 978-0-9554323-2-3

Andersen, Finn, *Guldet från växterna, Kristianstad boktryckeri*, 2004. ISBN 91-974063-7-6

www.wikipedia.org.uk

www.shenet.se